THEN, NOW AND TOMORROW

THEN, NOW AND TOMORROW

The Autobiography of a Communications Engineer

A Trilogy Comprising a Learning Life, a Professional Life and a Personal Life

John Bray

The Book Guild Ltd
Sussex, England

The Book Guild Ltd
25 High Street,
Lewes, Sussex

First published 1999
© John Bray 1999
Set in Times
Typesetting by
Acorn Bookwork, Salisbury, Wiltshire

Printed in Great Britain by
Bookcraft (Bath) Ltd, Avon

A catalogue record for this book is
available from the British Library

ISBN 1 85776 481 1

To my dear wife Margaret for her love and care, and a lifetime together of more than 60 years during which occurred most of the events described in this book.

CONTENTS

Preface – Why an Autobiography?   ix

PART 1   A LEARNING LIFE

1   Family and Early Days   3

2   Life as a Dockyard Apprentice 1927–32   11

3   A Student at City and Guilds
Engineering College, London 1932–35   20

4   The Choice of a Career: A Critical
Turning Point   26

References

PART 2   A PROFESSIONAL LIFE

1   Training at the PO Research Station,
Dollis Hill and Northern Ireland 1935   33

2   The Radio Services of the Post Office   35

3   The Radio Experimental Branch at
Dollis Hill 1936–54   38

4   The War Years 1939–45   42

5   Microwave Radio Communication   50

6   A Commonwealth Fund Fellowship in the
USA 1955–56   58

7   The Post Office and Television   63

8   The Inland Radio Branch: PO ED HQ
      1954–60   67

9   The Beginning of Satellite Communications:
      Space Communication Systems Branch
      PO ED HQ 1961–63   71

10   Technological Advances of the Postwar Years   83

11   The Research Branch at Dollis Hill: 1963–66   86

12   Director of Research and New Laboratories at
      Martlesham, Suffolk 1966–75   90

13   Professional Institutions   99

References   103

PART 3   A PERSONAL LIFE

1   Reading, Writing and Poetry   107

2   Love, Marriage and Children   116

3   We Move to East Anglia   123

4   A Sailing Hobby   126

5   Some Ideas, Not Yet Realised   132

6   Retirement and Community Life   140

7   The Women in My Life!   149

8   Politics   158

9   Religion and Cosmology   163

10   A Final Summing-up   169

References   171

INDEX   173

PREFACE

Why an Autobiography?

The decision to write an autobiography took a firm shape in my mind on 16 August 1996 when, a few weeks from my 86th birthday, I found myself in the Emergency Ward of Ipswich Hospital, following a disastrous car accident from which I was fortunate to escape alive, albeit with a broken leg, crushed ribs and miscellaneous bruises. In spite of the trauma of the accident and a realisation that I had been very near to leaving this world, I felt remarkably calm and, in the quiet peace of the hospital ward around midnight, began to realise that, not only was it a fortunate escape but that I had enjoyed a wonderful and fulfilled life for which in some way I ought to express thanks.

The weeks that followed in the hospital offered a marvellous opportunity to 'think and write' without significant interruption, from which came a draft outline of an autobiography and ideas later to be expanded.

The writing presented an opportunity to live again the happinesses and successes of a fulfilled life, to recall the occasional blows of fate and ponder their impact, and to put in order one's thoughts about the great imponderables of life – its purpose, the reality of God and the origin of the Universe. And what better way to use retirement when health or weather inhibited outdoor occupations!

This period of reflection underlined the influence that people, books and teachers had on the shape of things to come. They led ultimately in the author's case to an immensely rewarding professional career in research and development in telecommunications that spanned half a century and saw the introduction of microchip technology, digital techniques, communication satellites and optical fibre cables that have transformed world communications and heralded the introduction of the Internet and the World-Wide Web. It saw too the beginnings of sound and television broadcasting and the development of technologies that immensely improved the scope and quality of these services. It was the author's privilege to have been involved, directly or as a 'ringside spectator', in the research and development stages of most of these developments, over a period of some 40 years until his retirement in 1975 as Director of Research in the Post Office Engineering Department and British Telecom. His experience has thus given him a unique and direct view of 'how things happened' that may be of value as history, and thus worthy of inclusion in an autobiography.

But even scientists and engineers have a life outside technology – beginning in my case with a childhood in a family of limited means in Somerset more than 80 years ago, when the First World War was being fought. To retrace one's educational steps via the primary and secondary schools of the early 1900s, to an apprenticeship in Portsmouth Naval Dockyard and thence via scholarships to Imperial College, London, has been a fascinating experience, offering some illuminating 'then' and 'now' comparisons and lessons.

And of course even scientists and engineers fall in love, write poetry, get married and bring up families – in my case during the hazards of the Second World War and the post-war years.

Hobbies are an important part of life – often a means of maintaining a degree of sanity and balance against the stresses of existence. Mine include omnivorous reading, a habit learned from my mother who, before the days of free public libraries, relied wholly on the Carnegie libraries of her day. But sailing and maintaining a sizeable wooden yacht became a major means of relaxation from 1960 to 1987. This theme, and the joys and hazards of sailing, form part of this autobiography, serving perhaps as a warning to others.

In retirement, voluntary community work in a rural environment proved a rewarding occupation – in my case looking after the financial and grant-aid matters involved in building and maintaining a new Village Hall, and committee work with Suffolk Community Council. And of course there is always, as with Voltaire, 'one's own garden to cultivate'.

The last chapters of the autobiography take up the theme mentioned earlier – an attempt to express in a more considered and orderly fashion one's views on politics, religion and cosmology.

To give a structure to these diverse themes I have divided my account into Part 1 'A Learning Life', which focuses on parents, childhood, schools and college, Part 2 'A Professional Life', concerned primarily with the remarkable advances in communications technology of the last half-century, and Part 3 'A Personal Life', which deals with marriage and children, writing and poetry, hobbies and views on religion, politics and cosmology. Clearly, these to some extent overlap, as will become apparent as my story proceeds.

PART 1
A LEARNING LIFE

1

Family and Early Days

Parents

The Institution of Electrical Engineers once sent out a questionnaire asking about factors that had influenced their members about their choice of a career in electrical engineering – I had no hesitation in replying that in my case a major factor was undoubtedly my parents, the family background and the encouragement that they provided. In this I was singularly fortunate; my parents were far from wealthy but they had a firm belief in the value of education and the need for hard work – the Protestant 'work ethic' – to achieve a success in life. For this, and their love of their children, my brother and I have every reason to be grateful. (See plate 1)

My mother, née Emily Eliza Clothier, was a great reader and from her I inherited a love of books and reading; from both parents there came a sound constitution that enabled me to live healthily well into my 80s. Her father had been a farm worker in Somerset who died in his 30s as a result of the harsh working conditions of farm labourers in his day, leaving five daughters and a crippled son to be brought up at a time when social security was nonexistent. Her mother, my maternal grandmother, maintained her family by having the girls work at home on a 'cottage industry' basis for the glove-making industry then flourishing in Yeovil. Their crippled son, my uncle Jack, was largely self-taught, and by his energy and determination became a reader on the staff of the *Western Gazette* newspaper, then published in Yeovil.

My father, William James Bray, after early days in Lewes,

3

Sussex, where he helped in the early 1900s to repair some of the first motor cars to be seen on the roads, joined the Royal Navy a few years before the outbreak of the First World War. He first saw war service as an Engine-room Artificer in the destroyers of the Dover Patrol and later in gunboats on the Euphrates, Mesopotamia (now Iraq).

He saw the scuttling of the German fleet at Scapa Flow in 1918, and while there made a fine model of a triple-expansion reciprocating steam engine and a water-tube steam boiler, capable of propelling a fair-sized yacht, as a present for his sons! On retirement from the Navy he worked for a time at the Admiralty Surface Weapons Research Establishment at Portsdown, but was called up at the outbreak of the Second World War in 1939 for service on destroyers protecting the Atlantic convoys – a tough assignment for a man of his age.

My father had little formal education and taught himself his craft of the maintenance of reciprocating steam engines and steam turbines, largely from correspondence courses. I am grateful to him for, amongst many other things, his encouragement to study what he called the 'whys and wherefores' of the engineering world around me.

I first saw the light of day on 10 September 1911, at Fratton, Portsmouth. During the First World War, when my father was mainly overseas, my parents moved to my grandmother's home in Yeovil, where my early childhood was spent. My mother doubtless encouraged me to read at a very early age – I cannot remember not being able to! My engineering instincts were also developed at an early age – by gifts of ever more advanced sets of the construction toy Meccano for birthday anniversaries and at Christmas.

An event of great importance in my young life was the opening of the first public library in Yeovil – I can still remember the thrill of seeing such a splendid variety of brand-new books which could be borrowed free of charge! And the new world of science fiction that opened up when chance led me to H.G. Wells's *First Men on the Moon*.

Schools

After the end of the war the family found a new home in Milton, Portsmouth, and my education was continued in Milton Primary School where, in spite of over-large classes by today's standards, dedicated teachers gave me every encouragement to study for the entrance examination to a secondary school. I remember a pleasant task each month was to help with the preparation of a 'scrapbook' of articles, poems and drawings contributed by members of the class. At the end of the month the scrapbook was read and displayed to the whole class, with much gratification to the authors of stories (of whom I was sometimes one) and the painters of pictures.

Success in the entrance examination at 11-plus gained a place at Portsmouth Southern Secondary School[1]* and the traditional reward of a bicycle – almost a necessity for the journey from home at Milton to the school in Southsea. At an early stage pupils were to some extent 'streamed' into the academics and those destined for more practical futures such as the Portsmouth Naval Dockyard.

Sport and team games did not feature highly on the agenda of the Southern Secondary School so, happily, I was free to enjoy cycling and walking with friends in the pleasant Hampshire countryside, and swimming off Eastney Beach.

However, the school had a fine tradition of producing each year a Gilbert and Sullivan opera on the South Parade Pier, Southsea – an enjoyable activity in which the whole school, masters and boys, participated. I recall being invited for an audition for the chorus of *The Pirates of Penzance*, asked to sing up and down the musical scale and being told politely, 'Yes, thank you, that will do. You will be selling programmes on Mondays, Wednesdays and Fridays'!

It was about this time that I began to discover as a teenager the joys of classical music from a performance of *Lilac Time* in the Theatre Royal, Southsea – an experience that left me with

---

* References Part 1 pp. 28–29

a love of Schubert's music – especially the great C Major symphony – that has grown and lasted a lifetime.

Grandparents

As I mentioned earlier, my maternal grandmother Caroline Clothier had a major role in maintaining single-handed a large family – an example of rugged independence and making the best of things that could hardly be bettered. (See plate 3) And she was a splendid cook – I can still taste her marvellous hot apple tarts, served with clotted cream and much enjoyed after a walk with my crippled uncle Jack in his self-propelled invalid chair around the pleasant Somerset countryside.

My paternal grandmother was a small lady who in her younger days had been a dairymaid on a large estate near Bristol. Sadly, later in life she suffered from severe deafness, and it was a pleasure to me as a schoolboy to build for her a valve amplifier radio that enabled her to listen via headphones to her favourite church services and music.

My paternal grandfather, William James Bray, was very much my hero and in some degree a role model. (See plate 2) He was something of a 'character', having left home in Bideford, Somerset, at a very early age, probably against his parents' wishes, to join the Navy. He became a sailmaker, well-versed in working at considerable heights on the sails of the square-rigged ships of his day. He sailed round the world in the Flying Squadron of the Navy, and was in India at the time of Queen Victoria's Durbar in Delhi – a highlight of his life.

On his retirement from the Navy he worked for a time in the Sussex County Prison at Lewes as a Warder, where his powerful physique and determination helped to subdue violent and unruly prisoners. And yet he was in reality a gentle and courageous man, well loved by my father, his two daughters and grandsons. Later he came to live in Southsea, where his sail-making skill enabled him to get work making tents and marquees, whilst his ability to work at heights was put to use in erecting flags and flagpoles. One of his hobbies was making model ships in bottles; his skill with the needle was put to use in making undergarments for his wife and daughters!

He died at the age of 78, a physically strong man who could have lived for much longer but for his distrust of naval doctors who might have treated him for the severe dental pyorrhoea from which he suffered.

Family Tree

The Bray family archives contain a 'Family Tree' which begins with a John Sanders of Chittlehampton, Devon, whose daughter Mary Jane Sanders married a William James Bray in the mid-19th century.

The St Hieritas Churchyard at Chittlehampton contains gravestones with the following names:

Jane Bray 1824 – 1908, age 84 years
John Bray 1826 – 1908, age 82 years
Elizabeth Bray 1846 – 1914, age 68 years
Edwin Bray 1854 – 1919, age 65 years

It is encouraging to note the ages thus recorded, at a time when average ages were a good deal less, and interesting to see the recurrence of family christian names (my younger daughter was named Elizabeth).

The Schoolboy Discovers Broadcasting

During my schooldays in the 1920s radio broadcasting was just beginning under the direction of Sir John Reith and the Chief Engineer, Captain P.P. Eckersley. The London transmitter, call sign 2LO, was followed by the first of the regional transmitters, 6BM at Bournemouth – the latter was some 30 miles from my home at Southsea and within range of a simple crystal receiver.

For my mother, living in a home that could not afford a gramophone and records or attendance at concerts, and for

7

millions of other people too, sound radio broadcasting opened up a magical new world of music, talk by interesting people and entertainment. In today's world – oversaturated with sound and television broadcasting – it is difficult now to realise what a momentous advance in the quality of life this represented.

Schoolboys in my day soon discovered a marvellous new hobby – the construction of crystal radio receivers, an operation that involved the expenditure of much of one's limited pocket money on enamelled copper wire for solenoid or 'honeycomb' coils for inductors, brass and mica sheet to make capacitors and wire for aerials.

Grandfather, with his roof-climbing abilities, played a useful role in erecting the almost mandatory 100ft-long aerial from chimney top to garden flagpole. However, to his dying day he refused to believe that the voices and music he heard in the headphones attached to the crystal set came from further afield than the Pier at Southsea!

Not content with headphones, I embarked on an ambitious project to build a non-valve amplifier – the first radio valves were far too expensive for a schoolboy's pocket! The solution arrived at was to attach a miniature microphone to the diaphragm of a telephone earpiece and link its electrical output via an audio transformer and a battery to a home-made loudspeaker created from another telephone earpiece driving a large pleated paper diaphragm. This contraption actually worked and taught one something about 'power gain' but also about the 'non-linearity' that produced audio distortion.

Then came a stimulating development – the discovery in my local library in Milton of a book called *The Boy Electrician* by A.P. Morgan and O. Carpenter, first published in 1920.[2] It was a remarkable book which not only instructed youngsters in the building of model electric motors, telephones, batteries and the like, but also showed them how to make and calibrate voltmeters and ammeters, make standard cells, standard resistors and measurements of resistance using a home-made Wheatstone bridge. And this with the simplest of materials within range of a schoolboy's pocket!

By this time my father had built a shed at the end of our

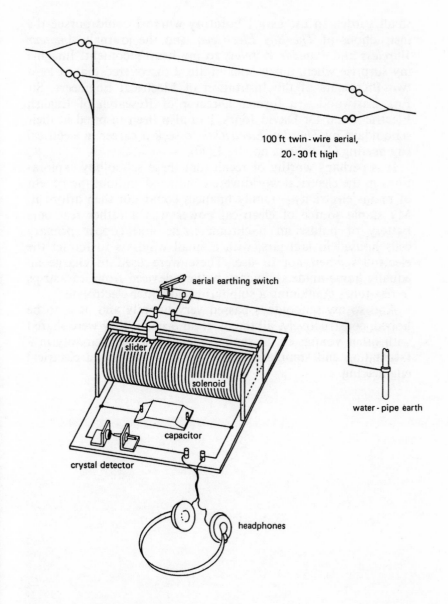

100 ft twin - wire aerial,
20 - 30 ft high

aerial earthing switch

slider

solenoid

water - pipe earth

capacitor

crystal detector

headphones

Crystal radio receiver (c. 1925)

small garden to use as a laboratory where I could pursue the instructions of *The Boy Electrician* and the journals *Amateur Wireless* and *Popular Wireless* to my heart's content. Imagine my surprise when, much later in life, I discovered that at least two Presidents of the Institution of Electrical Engineers, Sir Eric Eastwood – a former Director of Research of English Electric – and Dr David Jones, had also been inspired in their schooldays by *The Boy Electrician* to seek a career in electrical engineering (*IEE News* no. 48, 1990).

It is perhaps worthy of recall that these schoolboy explorations in the electrical world were conducted without the benefit of mains electricity – family finances could not then afford it. My staple source of electrical power was a rather fearsome battery of potassium bi-chromate/zinc and copper primary cells housed in jam jars, with a small windlass to retract the electrodes when not in use. These were used to charge an equally home-made secondary battery devised from lead strips in test tubes containing a sulphuric acid/water electrolyte.

And so my schooldays passed very happily and, it is to be hoped, constructively, all the more so because they were shared with other youngsters of similar age all finding their way in a fascinating and stimulating new world of radio and electrical engineering.

2

Life as a Dockyard Apprentice 1927–32

My schooling at the Portsmouth Southern Secondary School, with its bias towards mathematics, physics, chemistry and mechanics, provided a useful background for taking the entrance examination for Naval Dockyards in 1927. This was a three-day competitive Civil Service Commission examination, followed by an interview. The subjects taken were arithmetic, mathematics (including trigonometry and algebra to quadratic equations), history, geography, English grammar and composition, and English literature based on the study of a set book – all for a craft apprenticeship! Incidentally, some enlightened and kindly Civil Service Examiner had chosen Buchan's *The Thirty-Nine Steps* as one of the set books in the English part of the examination in my year, to the delight of the would-be apprentices but much to the disgust of Dr Parks, then Headmaster of the Southern Secondary School! However, I did well enough in the examination and interview to be able to choose 'electrical fitter', rather than 'mechanical fitter' or 'shipwright', for my future career, a highly significant decision as things turned out.

And thus in 1927 I became a properly indentured apprentice, and my parents committed contractually with 'My Lords of the Admiralty' to ensure that I completed satisfactorily a five-year course of training in the Dockyard workshops, on Naval ships and in the Dockyard School. (See plate 4) The working hours were from 7 am to 5.30 pm, Monday to Friday, and 7 am to 12.30 on Saturday; attendance at the School was on the basis of two afternoons in Admiralty time and three evenings in the apprentice's own time. All in all, quite a strenuous life for youngsters, compared with today's standards.

11

The Royal Dockyard Schools

The Dockyard Schools, which were located in the Portsmouth, Devonport, Chatham, Sheerness and Rosyth Dockyards, deserve special mention.[3]

They were first set up in the 1840s to overcome the poor educational standard of shipwright apprentices in the Naval dockyards. By the end of the century the Schools had progressed far beyond the limited aims for which they had been created and had developed into high-calibre technical colleges, catering not only for shipwrights but also for electrical and mechanical engineering apprentices, some of whom later found careers far outside the Admiralty service. Nevertheless, the main function of the Schools was to provide the craftsmen, chargehands, foremen and engineers of the Yards with the theoretical background and engineering understanding necessary for the efficient execution of their work. At the same time it aimed to equip suitable apprentices for promotion to professional engineering posts in the Admiralty service, in a limited number of cases via advanced training at the Royal Naval College, Greenwich, to become Admiralty Naval Constructors.

The intake of apprentices was divided into a Lower and an Upper School, depending initially on the degree of academic ability demonstrated at the entry examination. Progression from each year to the next of the four-year course depended on the result achieved in the annual examinations; of an intake of, say, 200 apprentices in the first year only some 20 might survive to the fourth-year Upper School, where the academic standard was equivalent to that of a university degree, although not formally recognised as such. Even this number of highly qualified apprentices was more than sufficient to meet the need for Admiralty professional engineers, and many of the fourth-year apprentices looked to careers outside the Admiralty service or to scholarships such as the Royal or Whitworth to continue their education to more advanced levels at a university.

The four-year course consisted of basic subjects such as mathematics, mechanics, metallurgy and heat engines, together

12

with subjects appropriate to each class of apprentice, such as electrical engineering, mechanical engineering, ship design and construction.

It was through the teaching at the Dockyard School that I became aware of the fascination and power of the higher mathematics – notably the differential and integral calculus, Bessel functions and the like. By chance I came across E.T. Bell's *Men of Mathematics*[4], which, by its emphasis on the mathematicians as well as their work, revealed mathematics as a creative and challenging human activity. The challenge was illustrated, for example, by story of Fermat and his 'Last Theorem', which he stated in the margin of his text and claimed to have proved, but did not include the formal proof because of insufficient space. The challenge to find a proof has taken eminent mathematicians several decades to achieve – and only in 1996 was one found! It was this approach, of describing innovation in terms of its creators, that led me to follow a similar approach in my book *The Communications Miracle*[5].

I greatly enjoyed my Portsmouth Dockyard School experience and owe much to the masters for their encouragement, in particular to Mr J.M. Irvine, the Headmaster, and Mr McKenzie, the Deputy Head. With uncharacteristic modesty I have to admit that I emerged with a useful collection of book prizes and winner of the Admiral Donaldson Cup as 'Top Apprentice of all Yards'! It was Mr McKenzie who laid on some out-of-hours extra classes in 'Heat, Light and Sound' to enable my Oxford and Cambridge School Leaving Certificate, gained at the Portsmouth Southern Secondary School, to qualify for an Intermediate BSc degree. This in turn later enabled me to complete my university college BSc course after two years, instead of three, and proceed to an MSc in the college third year.

It was this same Mr McKenzie, a Scot but not 'dour', who advised me, as a fledgling 20-year-old, to 'keep my family under my hat for a time' and choose, as an Admiralty book prize, Galsworthy's *Forsyte Saga* to provide a window on a world beyond my technical studies!

Life on the Dockyard Shop Floor

The practical tuition in the Dockyard was excellent in scope and quality, comprising work in the machine shop, electrical workshop, armature winding shop, meter test house and drawing office, and on board ships in dry dock. In the fifth year one might, with luck, participate in sea trials of newly refitted surface ships and submarines.

Two aspects of apprenticeship days in Portsmouth Dockyard stand out in retrospect – firstly the interest and even pride shown by the ordinary Yard fitters, each of whom might have an apprentice in his care, and secondly the freedom the apprentices had in their final years to move about the Yard to study and seek information on engineering work in progress on ships and in workshops.

It was the custom, approved by the Admiralty, for the first hour or two of the morning shift to be used by apprentices to work at their School studies in some 'cubby hole' in a workshop or unused cabin on a ship under refit, each with the full knowledge of their fitter and charge-hand. The 'cubby holes' I used ranged from one in a noisy boiler construction shop to one in the 'spotting top' of the ill-fated *HMS Hood*, then under refit, with a glorious view over the Dockyard. This habit of concentration for study in sometimes noisy or distracting situations no doubt became a useful skill for later in life.

The fitters took a keen interest in 'their' charges' progress in the Dockyard School examinations – and it was not unknown for bets to be placed on the outcome! This interest extended also to ensuring that their apprentice got a reasonable share of overtime cash payments and the like, and included welfare visits if the apprentice was ill or hurt in a workshop accident.

The work in the shops covered a wide range, from the stripping down and repair of ship-borne electrical equipment to the construction of new items, for example of radio equipment to Admiralty Signal School designs. Some of this work was on a 'piecework' basis, which produced not only a small but welcome addition to the pay packet but also an initiation into

14

the subtle arts of rate-setting and job-time estimation. The Drawing Office offered an interesting variety of work, ranging from the use of one's newly acquired knowledge of electrical theory to the design of simple electrical equipment and visits to ships being refitted to prepare 'as fitted' drawings.

Life in the Dockyard was not without its exciting incidents. One such occurred when working on the cruiser *HMS Dauntless*, then undergoing an extensive refit in dry dock. One cold winter morning a fire broke out on board, possibly due to overloading the temporary electrical power distribution switchboard by Dockyard 'matees'' electric coffee pots! I happened to be working on cable-laying in the cable tunnel in the bowels of the ship when the temporary lights went out and smoke began to fill the tunnel. After making my way in darkness, and with some trepidation, to the outside world with dozens of the 'matees' – it was to see, with some delight, a fire engine arrive on the dockside with the Admiral of the Dockyard, still clad in pyjamas, on board!

Taking part in sea trials in the later years of apprenticeship was undoubtedly one of the most stimulating and enjoyable, and perhaps educative, of an apprentice's activities. I still have mainly pleasant memories of the thrill of speed, turning and tilt trials of a re-fitted *HMS Dauntless* on sea trials in the English Channel. Somewhat less enjoyable was the job, usually given to apprentices, of measuring propeller shaft horsepower using a light-mirror shaft torsion meter in a cramped, hot-oil-smelling tunnel with everything vibrating wildly in speed trials and sea-sickness not far away.

But perhaps the most significant aspect of an apprenticeship training – not realised at the time – was the experience it gave of working in an adult world and, above all, of learning at first-hand how men on the shop floor think and react in given circumstances, knowledge that was to prove invaluable later in life in negotiation with staff representatives and trade unions.

Busy as was an apprentice's life, with much 'spare' time taken up by preparation for examinations, there was still time for hobbies. In my case this was predominantly 'radio' – a continuation of those schoolboy experiments but enhanced by

15

an apprentice's salary (small though it was) and the facilities afforded 'under the counter' by access to Dockyard workshops tools and scrap material. This was known by the name 'rabbiting', perhaps because any illegal items rapidly disappeared down various holes when a charge-hand or foreman came in sight!

Radio Hobbies

My first project was the building of a 'spark' radio transmitter with a spark coil built from the fine enamelled copper wire salvaged from discarded audio transformers. A fellow apprentice and I built matching tuned circuits that were energised from spark coils, and similar crystal receivers. With these and 100ft wire aerials, and in spite of a degree of uncertainty about the actual wavelength of our transmissions, we successfully communicated in Morse code over a distance of a few miles. All this was of course highly illegal and might have ended two fairly promising careers if the Post Office radio inspectors had been up to their job, but we did have the satisfaction of proving to ourselves that Marconi was on the right lines after all!

Now that a little more pocket money was available it became possible to purchase one's first radio valve – a 'dull emitter Triotron', an exciting next step that unfolded new possibilities for experiment. It was first deployed as an audio amplifier to drive a home-made pleated-paper diaphragm loudspeaker driven by a telephone earpiece, with a notable improvement in quality compared with the microphone amplifier in the schoolboy experiment described earlier.

The next experiment used the valve as an oscillator in a tuned circuit at about 20 MHz frequency (15 metres wavelength), feeding a half-wavelength dipole aerial. It was with a very real excitement that I saw for the first time a flash-lamp bulb in series with the aerial light up with radio-frequency current in what was a DC open-circuit!

From experiments with a single radio valve I progressed,

with some financial help from my father, to build a two-valve, crystal detector reflex super-heterodyne radio receiver, following a design by John Scott-Taggart (he was a prolific writer in the technical press in the early days of radio broadcasting; his blueprints for home-built radio receivers were widely used). The 'reflex' feature of the design was a great economy, for it enabled the same valve to function simultaneously as an audio and a radio-frequency amplifier.

It was about this time – the mid 1920s – that the Rice-Kellog moving-coil/conical diaphragm loudspeaker came on to the radio scene and demonstrated a remarkable improvement in sound quality compared with the earlier moving-iron armature and horn loudspeakers. It was my pride and joy to make my own moving-coil loudspeaker from Dockyard scrap material, including soft-iron pipe and copper wire for the electromagnet, and the use of a lathe in the Machine Shop to fashion the electro-magnet. And, with the aid of the facilities in the Dockyard Meter Test House, I was able to measure the magnetic flux in the moving coil gap and confirm that it corresponded with that derived from a calculation of the reluctance of the magnet circuit. Mounted on a 5ft square 'baffle board', this home-made moving-coil loudspeaker achieved a quality of sound reproduction that was unique at the time and brought visitors from afar to hear it!

Another project involved the making of a Baird-type spinning disc television receiver, with some help from the Dockyard Drawing Office to mark out a spiral of 30 scanning holes on the disc. The light source was a 'beehive' neon lamp, and the 2ft diameter spinning disc was driven by a small electric motor. The only television transmissions available were experimental ones from the 2LO London transmitter of the BBC, some 100 miles away. Nevertheless it was a triumph to see a live, postage-stamp size, flickering black-and-red image of a moving human head – this was the first real television, but even the most optimistic of innovators could hardly have imagined then the fantastic developments in television that the future held in store.

In retrospect, these 'extra-curricular' activities can be seen to have served a variety of purposes, valuable to an aspiring young engineer. For example, they provided convincing demonstrations of the validity of the scientific and engineering principles involved and the fact that, with a struggle, theory and practice could be made to converge. Even the economic aspects of design received attention, if only because of the limited depth of an apprentice's pocket!

Royal and Whitworth Scholarships

By the end of my fourth year as an apprentice the time had come to think seriously about my future. My experience to date had shown me the fascination and 'job satisfaction' of electrical engineering and convinced me that this was the career to pursue. But to reach the level that I sought demanded further advanced studies and a university degree. One door to this lay in the Royal and Whitworth Scholarships, which offered free tuition at a university and some financial support. The examination for these scholarships demanded degree-level standards in mathematics, science and engineering, including machine drawing. The Whitworth was aimed primarily at mechanical engineering students, the Royal included both electrical and mechanicals. My year, 1932, was unfortunate in that the Whitworth Committee decided, only a week or so before the actual examination, to exclude Dockyard electrical engineering apprentices on the grounds – mistaken – that their training in mechanical engineering was insufficient.

The preparatory work for the examination, which was common to both the Whitworth and Royal, included much working through of previous examination papers in what remained of one's free time. However, there was a certain intellectual pleasure in this since the engineering questions set by the examiners required not only engineering knowledge but the ability to apply known principles in ingenious and thought-demanding ways, somewhat akin to solving a *Times* crossword puzzle! The outcome, happily for me, was the award of a Royal scholarship to be held for three years at the City and

Guilds Engineering College, London. Furthermore, because of my father's Naval service, I was able to obtain a Kitchener Exhibition which provided some further assistance towards living expenses.

The fifth year of my Dockyard apprenticeship continued during the vacation periods of my three years at Guilds – some of it spent pleasantly and interestingly in telephone exchange maintenance at the Vernon Naval establishment, Portsmouth, and helping to lay submarine telephone cables between the Forts at Spithead!

3

A Student at City and Guilds Engineering College, London, 1932–35

History

The autumn of 1932 saw me enrolled as an undergraduate of the City and Guilds Engineering College, itself a constituent college of the Imperial College of Science and Technology, University of London, and part of the university complex in South Kensington initiated by Prince Albert in the reign of Queen Victoria. (See plate 5) The original City and Guilds of London Institute was established in 1878 by the Corporation of the City of London ('City') and certain of the London Livery Companies (the 'Guilds').

The City and Guilds College was located in Exhibition Road, Kensington, in a magnificent Victorian building (sadly no more) that would have delighted John Betjeman. And it was here that I spent very happily a good deal of the next three years of my life – in an environment dedicated to the study and advancement of science and engineering, but with congenial social overtones. The City and Guilds College comprised 'electrical', 'civil' and 'mechanical' departments; however some subjects, such as mathematics and science, which were common to all departments, were taught by the neighbouring Royal College of Science.

Since I already held an Intermediate BSc degree from my Dockyard days I was able to proceed to a two-year course for a Final degree.

Life as a Student at Guilds

I was fortunate in having an uncle and aunt living at Catford, who provided me with lodgings and company during term times. My daily journey to and from Guilds was initially by tram car to Victoria and thence by Underground to South Kensington – a slow and tedious journey, enlivened only in that the tram passed the Oval and in summertime one might catch glimpses of cricket!

With the purchase of a secondhand AJS motorcycle life became much more interesting, if not dangerous! Not only was the daily journey time shortened, but the possession of a motorcycle opened the door to the College Motor Club which, from time to time, held trials in the hilly areas of Sussex to demonstrate one's prowess in riding motorcycles over rough, steep and very muddy ground without actually falling off.

Lunches at College presented a problem for the 'scholarship' students, of whom there was a small group which included a few Dockyard apprentices. There was a Student Union lunch facility, but we had to 'watch our pennies' and survived on sandwiches provided by kind relatives or landladies. These we sometimes consumed in the neighbouring Science Museum, which offered not only erudition but excellent lunchtime music via the BBC and one of the first really hi-fi radio receivers. This was equipped with a magnificent 6ft by 6ft aperture exponential horn moving-coil loudspeaker, built into a wall of the Museum, and a *Wireless World* design of radio receiver with carefully proportioned band-pass tuned circuits that enabled an exceptionally wide audio-frequency response to be obtained.

The lunchtime concerts heard on this equipment were of outstanding sound quality that was a revelation to most of the listeners – one's memories may be coloured by nostalgia, but they always seemed to include Reginald Foort playing the organ at the Tower Ballroom, Blackpool! At any rate, they were much appreciated by my fellow students and myself as we munched our lunchtime sandwiches.

21

The Guilds Radio Society

I was delighted to find that the College had an active Radio Society with members at least as keen as I was to explore the fascinating new world of radio technology that was opening up before us. I became Secretary of the Radio Society in 1933, with responsibility for arranging lectures and visits of radio interest. During my time the members built, with the aid of the College's workshop, the Guild's first short-wave radio transmitter, call-sign G5YC. This was housed, with professorial agreement, in an attic room of the College with an aerial which I erected between the gables of the building – an activity that I feel sure Grandfather Bray, with his barefooted roof-climbing propensities, might well have approved. The call-sign G5YC achieved a certain notoriety in the world of radio amateurs in that its announcement was often accompanied by the sound of rushing waters, generated by pulling the chain of the toilet in the same attic room!

Amongst the lecturers I was able to persuade to talk to the Radio Society were some who later achieved considerable distinction in their careers. One such was Harold Bishop, later Sir Harold, Chief Engineer of the BBC and President of the Institution of Electrical Engineers, who lectured on 'Broadcasting'. Another was Robert Watson Watt, later Sir Robert who became famous for his role in the wartime development of radar. He talked to us about 'Radio-wave Research' at the Government Radio Research Station, Slough, of which he was then Head. We later visited Slough and saw work on the tracking of thunderstorms in distant parts of the world. This used two radio receiving stations, one in Cupar, Scotland, and the other at Slough, linked by a Post Office telephone line, enabling the radio signals generated by a thunderstorm and picked up by the two receivers to be displayed simultaneously on a cathode-ray tube, thus revealing its location. Although not strictly 'radar', this kind of research may well have triggered the development of the radio technique that had such a profound impact on the outcome of the Battle of Britain in the Second World War.

It was a privilege of the Secretary of the Radio Society to dine with the Lecturer and the Departmental Head of the College, then Professor C.L. Fortescue (later President of the Institution of Electrical Engineers), after the lecture and in the latter's comfortable home in Exhibition Road, South Kensington. To meet and talk with these interesting people in such surroundings was perhaps one of the most valuable parts of a college education.

Electrical Engineering Studies at Guilds

Professor Fortescue's lectures on electrical theory treated the subject in considerable depth and rigour, but in a manner that was both illuminating and thought-provoking. Some of the students found them heavy going, but fortunately my earlier training in electrical engineering in the Dockyard School had provided a good foundation that enabled me to follow and enjoy them. The 'Prof' had an endearing habit, in pausing for thought when writing complicated theory on the blackboard, of stepping backwards, chalk in hand, and swaying at the very edge of the raised dais on which he was standing!

My course work was biased towards 'light current' electrical engineering – largely centred on a text written by Dr E. Mallett of Guilds, entitled *Telegraphy and Telephony – Including Wireless*, with a sub-title 'An Introductory Textbook of the Science and Art of the Electrical Communication of Intelligence', published in 1929[6]. With some forethought my copy of this book had been presented to me by 'The Lords Commissioners of the Admiralty' in 1931 as a prize for progress in the Dockyard School.

I must have absorbed some of this erudition because, at the end of my first two years at Guilds, I emerged with a BSc (Eng), First-Class Honours degree and as an 'Associate of the City and Guilds of London Institute' (ACGI).

My third year at Guilds presented an opportunity to work for an MSc degree. The subject for a year's research came about almost fortuitously – I had observed in the course of a

23

first-degree project on a valve oscillator with a long solenoid inductor, that unwanted parasitic modes of oscillation, at much higher frequency than the designed mode, sometimes occurred. I suggested to Professor Fortescue that these might be worthy of further investigation, and he agreed but pointed out that it would have to be on a very small budget to buy any of the additional electrical components that might be necessary. He suggested that a suitable low-cost source might be in the junk shops of Lisle Street, Soho (also a notorious haunt of prostitutes), but coupled this with a stern warning to be careful of the 'ladies' who might be lurking in various doorways!

It is interesting to reflect that most of today's college students engaged in research expect, and are provided with, almost unlimited supplies of digital measuring equipment, data loggers, plotters and analysers, not to say computer facilities. We students in the 1930s had often to make and calibrate our own measuring equipment such as valve voltmeters, build our own experimental 'breadboards' and protect them from interference by using tin biscuit boxes as screens.

But life at Guilds was not all hard work. There were, for example, 'wars' with King's College, London – sometimes involving hosepipes to repel invaders of Guilds. In return, Guilds attempted to capture the famed skeleton of Jeremy Bentham at King's. And, apropos of 'biscuit tins', there was the occasion when the Guild's mascot – a De Dion-Bouton steam motor car of the early 1900s, known as 'Boanerges' – bore a group of Guilds students to Downing Street to protest at the alleged acceptance by the then Prime Minister, Ramsey MacDonald, of a motor car from Huntley and Palmers, the biscuit manufacturers! This activity resulted in some Guilds students appearing at, and being fined, at Bow Street Police Court.

My worst 'contretemps' was being fined a few pounds for 'damage to the steps of the Albert Memorial' during a Guy Fawkes celebration, part of a communal fine on the College and most unfair because I wasn't there!

So came to an end three enjoyable and rewarding years at Guilds, enriched by the companionship of a small group of

Dockyard apprentices who banded themselves in a club called the 'ex-4YAs' (ex-fourth-year apprentices association) which met annually for a dinner, chat and sing-song in the Chanticleer Restaurant in Soho. And, as mentioned earlier, I was able to return to Portsmouth Dockyard during college vacations to complete the fifth year of my apprenticeship.

My years at Guilds had added an MSc (Eng) degree and the 'Diploma of Imperial College' to my professional qualifications, and the time had come, in 1935, to consider seriously a future career. The times were not propitious – there was a great deal of unemployment and much competition, even at professional level, for jobs in engineering.

4

The Choice of A Career: A Critical Turning-Point

An Interview with the Post Office

A chance meeting with a friend, then employed in the
Engineering Department of the Post Office, at a meeting of the
'ex-4YA' Dockyard ex-apprentices association in 1935 drew
my attention to a forthcoming Civil Service Open Competition
for Assistant Engineers in the PO ED. He spoke highly of the
work and the prospects for promotion in the ED, and encouraged me to apply.

Entrants to the competition were required to have an
Honours degree in engineering or a related subject, such as
physics, chemistry or mathematics. Competition for the dozen
posts offered proved to be severe, with more than a hundred
applicants. However, I filled in the necessary application
forms, enlisted the help of referees from Guilds and the
Dockyard School, and was eventually invited to an interview.

The Chairman of the Interview Board, although I did not
know it at the time, was Mr A.J. Gill (later Sir Archibold Gill),
Chief Engineer of the Post Office Engineering Department, in
many ways a kindred spirit since he had been an apprentice in
a shipbuilding yard in the North of England. Apart from my
falling over the mat in nervousness as I entered the interview
room, the interview at first went smoothly but unspectacularly,
with the usual questions on school, college, apprenticeship-
training and hobbies. The latter brought radio into the
questioning and then, from A.J. Gill, came the 64,000 dollar
question – 'Do you believe in the objective existence of the
sidebands of a modulated carrier wave?'

Today all good radio engineers would have no hesitation in saying 'yes', but in the 1920s there were two schools of thought, much debated in the Institution of Electrical Engineers.

One school, inspired by Professor Fleming of University College, London (inventor of the thermionic valve), considered that sidebands were merely a convenient mathematical fiction; another school under Professor Fortescue of City and Guilds College claimed that they had objective existence and could be demonstrated experimentally. This in fact he had shown students at Guilds in a demonstration involving a sine-wave modulated carrier-wave oscillator, a tuned circuit the resonant frequency of which could be swept by a rotating capacitor and an oscilloscope to display the amplitude of the response of the tuned circuit. The pattern on the oscilloscope screen was in the form of a triple-peaked curve – the larger being the carrier wave and the peaks on either side the lower and upper sidebands. So it was with a sense of triumph that I replied, 'Yes, I have seen them [the sidebands]!'

The smile on A.J. Gill's face as good as told me that the job was mine, and so indeed it proved when I was later asked to attend the Post Office Engineering Department Headquarters at Alder House in St Martin's Lane, London, to be posted as a 'Probationary Assistant Engineer.

Admiralty or Post Office?

Almost at the same time as I received an offer of an Assistant Engineer post in the Post Office ED, there came an offer from the Admiralty of further training leading to an Assistant Constructorship in the Admiralty service.

Top apprentices from the combined dockyards list of the fourth-year midsummer examination were selected for advanced training at the RN College, Greenwich, which led to their appointment as Assistant Naval Constructors responsible for the design, construction and maintenance of the ships and shore establishments of the Navy. During their time at the

27

College these selected apprentices wore Naval Officer's uniform and spent some time at sea.

With my family background of naval service from Napoleonic times and during two World Wars and my own liking for the sea, this was a very attractive proposition. But as a teenager I had, like many of my contemporaries, been much influenced by anti-war books and plays such as R.C. Sherriff's *Journey's End* and its agonising picture of trench warfare in the First World War, Remarque's *All Quiet on the Western Front* and Theodore Dreiser's *Kaiser's Coolies* and its account of war as seen from the German Navy. In my youthful optimism I looked forward to a world free from major wars and one in which one's energies could more usefully be employed in activities and services of greater benefit to mankind than the continued construction of the engines of war.

And so, 'for better or for worse', but certainly 'for richer or for poorer', I decided to opt for the Post Office Engineering Department.

Nearly 50 years later I have no reason to regret this decision, which led to a career full of interest, challenge and great fulfilment. But sometimes I still wonder whether those 'sidebands' might not have been the magical key to it all!

References

(1) *Portsmouth Southern Grammar School for Boys*, by A.C. Hitchins, MA; a history of the school from 1888 to 1954; printed by Coasby Ltd, Southsea, c.1955
(2) *The Boy Electrician* by A.P. Morgan and O. Carpenter; pub. Harrap, 1920; second edition by A.P. Morgan and J.W. Sims pub. Harrap, 1930
(3a) *The Royal Dockyard Schools* by K.H. Allen; pub. Institution of Electrical Engineers, Engineering Science and Education Journal, History of Technology, August, 1996
(3b) *A History of Apprentice Training in HM Dockyard Portsmouth* by S.W.B. Leathlean, pub. Hampshire County Museum Service, 1990
(4) *Men of Mathematics* by E.T. Bell; pub. Victor Gollancz, 1937

(5) *The Communications Miracle – the Telecommunication Pioneers from Morse to the Information Superhighway* by John Bray; pub. Plenum, London and New York, 1995

(6) *Telegraphy and Telephone – Including Wireless*, by Dr E. Malett; pub. Chapman and Hall, London, 1929

PART 2

A PROFESSIONAL LIFE

In Part 2 I look back at, and comment on, some of the remarkable developments in worldwide telecommunications and broadcasting that have occurred in the last half-century – mainly from the viewpoint of the innovators themselves, the significance of their contributions and their likely impact on the future of mankind.

It has been my good fortune to have been either to some degree involved in, or to have witnessed as a ringside observer, many of these developments. These advances have been made possible mainly by the creation of new technology, described for example in my book *The Communications Miracle*[1]*; they have been accompanied by major developments in the political and commercial management of change and the battle between public control, and private enterprise and competition[2].

My own career involvement in the Post Office began in 1935 with induction course training for Probationary Assistant Engineers, then located at the PO Research Station, Dollis Hill, north-west London, near the Welsh Harp at Hendon.

---

* References Part 2 pp. 103–104

1

Training at the PO Research Station, Dollis Hill, and Northern Ireland 1935

The induction class at Dollis Hill comprised some 20 students, including some who had passed a 'Limited' Competition, i.e. one limited to staff already employed by the PO, as well as the six 'Open Competition' entrants, of whom I was one. (See plate 6)

The interesting and thorough training course comprised lectures by specialists from various branches of the PO Engineering Department, practical training on the installation and maintenance of various types of telephone and telegraph, transmission and exchange switching equipment, and visits to PO plant and establishments in the field.

However, some of the students found one lecturer rather long-winded and one of them discovered an ingenious way of stepping on the hands of the electric clock in the lecture theatre by means of a concealed on-off switch in the clock cable. The increasingly worried frown on the face of this lecturer as the clock time moved inexorably on and his remaining time unexpectedly shortened had to be seen to be believed!

On completion of the course at Dollis Hill we were given further training in PO Regions of our choice. I opted for Northern Ireland, where I had a favourite uncle, a teacher in a technical college in Lisburn, who kindly offered lodging and company. It was at Telephone House, Belfast, that I first met Gilbert Metson, then an Area Engineer but who was also studying part-time for a PhD degree at Queen's University, Belfast. Dr Metson later had a distinguished career in research

33

at the PO Research Station at Dollis Hill, where he became Director of Research and was my predecessor in this post.

However, in 1935 Gilbert Metson was my tutor in PO Area work and practice. The Province was, as ever, subject to terrorist violence, and indeed my arrival at Telephone House, Belfast, coincided with bomb damage, fortunately small, to the building. I recall Gilbert's sage advice on the realities of life in Ulster:

– never mix Catholics and Protestants in the same gang.
– if you see a Union Jack on a telephone pole, leave it!

My life in the Northern Ireland Post Office Region was going smoothly, and I was beginning to enjoy Area engineering work, when there came a telegram requiring me to report to Dr Walmsley, Assistant Engineer-in-Chief of the Post Office, at ED Headquarters in London. He informed me that there was an Assistant Engineer post vacant in the Radio Experimental Branch of the ED at the Research Station, Dollis Hill – would I like to take it?

The opportunity to combine what had been a hobby with experimental work in radio on a professional plane – and what was more, getting paid for it – was irresistible, and so my reply was an unhesitating 'Yes, thank you!' And so began a new phase in my career that was full of interest and involved work with a significant impact on the development of worldwide radio communication.

2

The Radio Services of the Post Office

Post Office involvement in the world of radio, as I saw it in 1936 when I joined the Radio Experimental Branch of the ED, covered many aspects and was on an impressive scale. The services provided by radio ranged from worldwide telephone and telegraph communication between land-based stations and with ships at sea on the far oceans of the globe, to shorter-range communication with coastal shipping via the Post Office network of coast radio stations.

Although there existed a worldwide network of submarine telegraph cables dating from Victorian times, these were of limited capacity; intercontinental submarine telephone cables did not become available until the late 1950s. Until then telephone communication between the UK and the USA was limited to ten or so circuits of limited reliability carried by short-wave radio, and one long-wave radio circuit. These were manually operated via the PO International Exchange; there was often a waiting time, speech quality was uncertain and the calls were costly, but the service was invaluable and in great demand.

The scale and scope of PO radio-engineering projects was impressive by any standard. The long-wave radio-telegraph transmitter GBR at Rugby, operating on the remarkably low radio frequency of 16 kHz, was one of the most powerful radio transmitters in the world, providing broadcast telegraph Press and News services and time signals from the Royal Observatory at Greenwich to land stations and ships at sea throughout the globe. Its vast aerial array, carried on twelve 800ft-high masts, extended over two miles, and radiated radio waves of

18,750 metres wavelength. These waves are so long, crest to crest, that they propagate freely by diffraction round the Earth's curved surface and are guided between the lower electrified layers of the ionosphere and earth, from Rugby to its antipodes on the far side of the globe.

Another high-power transmitter GBY, operating on a frequency of 50 kHz, wave length 6,000 metres, provided a single telephone circuit between the UK and USA; known as the 'TAT' – the Transatlantic Telephone – it was opened in 1926. It was particularly valuable in that it provided until the 1950s a reliable circuit even when the short-wave radio circuits, transmitted by ionospheric reflection, were disrupted by solar (sun-spot) activity. However, in this part of the radio spectrum, which had to be shared with several countries, there was room only for a single telephone circuit.

Until the advent of the first transatlantic submarine telephone cable in 1956, all long-distance intercontinental telephone traffic had to be carried on short radio waves, i.e. between about 10 and 30 metres wavelength, 30 to 10 MHz frequency. The wider space available in this part of the radio spectrum compared with long waves enabled more telephone circuits to be provided – but even so, only some ten circuits were available between the UK and USA. However, the transmitter powers and aerial sizes required were smaller than for the long-wave radio stations and the cost of provision correspondingly less.

Because these radio circuits were the only method of telephone communication between the UK and USA, Australia, New Zealand and other countries until the late 1950s – and were correspondingly important both commercially and socially – much research and development effort went into improving by technical means their quality and reliability. And this, for more than a decade, became the theme of much of my work in the Radio Experimental Branch of the Post Office Engineering Department.[1][3]

The PO Engineering Department also provided technical support to the Post Office Adminstration, headed by the Postmaster General at the Headquarters in St Martins le Grand, London.

The PO, on behalf of Parliament, was responsible for the regulation and control of radio broadcasting, for example for the allocation of wavelengths/frequencies for broadcasting and other radio transmitters, the licensing of radio receivers and the collection of licence fees, the control of radio interference and the detection of illegal radio transmitters.

These responsibilities produced a host of technical problems, some needing rapid solutions, that only scientific and engineering expertise could provide. The advent of television broadcasting in 1936 involved the determination of technical standards, a field that became increasingly complex and demanding of science, as well as technology, when colour television arrived in the 1960s.

In many of these developments there were profound international overtones that required solution via the ITU, the International Telecommunication Union at Geneva, and its Consultative Committees for Telephone, Telegraph and Radio. These concerned international standardisation of technical standards to facilitate the interconnection of national telegraph and telephone systems by cable and radio, the interchange of television programmes between broadcasters and the allocation of radio frequencies to avoid interference. In all these there was active involvement between the PO Administration and the PO ED, its Radio and Research Branches.

But the new, almost science fiction, field of microchips, digital techniques, communication satellites, optical fibre cables and information technology lay all in the future. Little did I, as a schoolboy building crystal radio sets in 1927, even as a new entrant to the PO ED in 1935, have the remotest idea of the kind of technological future that lay before us.

3

The Radio Experimental Branch at Dollis Hill 1936–54

When I joined it in 1936 the Radio Experimental Branch at Dollis Hill was headed by Albert Mumford, later Sir Albert, Engineer-in-Chief of the Post Office and former President of the Institution of Electrical Engineers. To Sir Albert and his deputy Captain Charles Booth I owe a debt of gratitude for their insistence on regular, carefully written reports stating clearly the objectives and progress on the experimental work each group under their command had in hand. From this one learned the value of the Baconian dictum 'Reading maketh a full man, writing an exact man' and formed a habit that served well over a lifetime.

The radio developments outlined in this chapter are described in more technical detail in my books *The Communications Miracle*[1] and *Memoirs of a Telecommunications Engineer*[3]; the aim here is to identify and outline the more important developments and indicate their significance.

Perhaps the most significant from a commercial point of view was the conversion of the transatlantic and other short-wave radio links, initially operated on a double-sideband basis (dsb), to single-sideband (ssb) operation (thus demonstrating yet again the reality of the sidebands of an amplitude modulated carrier-wave!).

In single-sideband operation either the upper or the lower sideband of an amplitude modulated carrier wave was selected and the carrier wave itself was reduced to a fraction of its normal level, before transmission. At the receiver the residual

38

carrier was selected, amplified and used to demodulate the chosen sideband to audio frequency.

Single-sideband, reduced-carrier operation of short-wave radio links realised significant improvements compared with dsb:

- a signal-to-noise improvement of 9 decibels, equivalent to increasing the transmitter power eight times, by avoiding the waste of power in the carrier in dsb;
- an improvement in voice quality by avoiding the non-linear distortion that occurs in dsb under multi-path transmission conditions;
- two independent (isb) telephone channels could be accommodated in each dsb frequency allocation.

The selection of the sidebands and the carrier wave was made practicable by the development of wave filters using quartz crystals as resonators, pioneered by the Bell Telephone Laboratories, USA. At Dollis Hill the design and manufacture of such filters, including the quartz resonators, was already in progress in 1936 for the multi-channel carrier cable systems then being developed.

From this work were designed ssb receivers, installed at the PO Receiving Station, Baldock, Herts, and ssb transmitter drives, installed at the PO Transmitting Station, Rugby. The first commercial use of ssb was on the transatlantic route, in co-operation with the American Telephone and Telegraph Company. During the war years the fighting services also converted their main short-wave communication links to ssb, using the PO designs and equipment made by the Marconi Company.

A research tool that proved useful in the development of speech privacy and carrier telegraph systems for use on short-wave links was an 'Artificial Fading Machine' that realistically simulated the multi-path transmission, produced by multiple reflection from the ionosphere, that arises on such links. It enabled speech privacy systems to be tested without 'putting them on the air' – and revealing their characteristics to an enemy. Carrier telegraph systems could be tested in a repeatable manner and assessed quantitatively for their ability to combat short-wave fading.

Perhaps the most exciting development was the PO multiple-unit steerable antenna (MUSA) short-wave receiving system at Cooling Marshes, Kent, and its American ATT counterpart at Manahawkin, New Jersey, USA. This was the most complex and extensive short-wave receiving system ever built for commercial use – it represented a last, almost despairing, attempt to improve the quality and reliability of transatlantic telephone communication before the advent of the first submarine telephone cable, some 15 years later.

The MUSA comprised an in-line array of 16 horizontal rhombic aerials, stretching two miles over the Cooling Marshes on a great-circle path to the USA, and linked by coaxial cables to the receiving centre. The 16 received signals, after conversion to an intermediate frequency, could be adjusted in phase to add thus improving the signal-to-noise power ratio by 16 times (12 db). The sharp vertical plane directivity of the MUSA – a degree or two beamwidth – enabled individual ray paths of, say, a three-hop and a four-hop signal to be separated. The audio signals corresponding to each path could then be combined after correction for the time delay, perhaps a millisecond or so, between the two paths.

The MUSA concept originated in the Bell Telephone Laboratories, New Jersey, under the direction of Dr H.T. Friis – and for a young engineer such as I it was a most inspiring and educative project in which to be involved.

The MUSA had an important role in the war years – it was the only channel by which President Roosevelt and Prime Minister Churchill could converse directly – using of course the best speech privacy equipment then available. And it carried the voices of American commentators – including the legendary Raymond Gram Swing – which did much to boost British morale.

My colleagues and I who were struggling to complete the MUSA at Cooling in the first year of the war did derive some benefit from our work. Local opinion had it that we were constructing a 'death-ray' machine to bring down German bombers whose route lay along the Thames estuary to London and, out of gratitude, resulted in quite a few free pints of beer in the local pub!

4

The War Years 1939–45

By the outbreak of war in September 1939 many of the Radio and Research Branch staff at Dollis Hill were already involved in urgent war work of various kinds, often on a six- or seven-day a week basis, whilst others volunteered to join the fighting services or were seconded to various Defence establishments.

In a war in which science and technology had a vital role, the skills and knowledge available amongst the scientists and engineers of the Post Office were of particular value; there is no doubt that they made a major contribution to the final victory over Germany and Japan.

The Research Station at Dollis Hill became a focal point in the national defence strategy; the Lines Branch of the PO ED moved there from its London City Headquarters into a new reinforced and windowless building, and a bomb-proof underground building known as 'The Paddocks' was constructed on the site to house the wartime Cabinet, should its home in the Houses of Parliament be destroyed by enemy action.

The Station itself, in view of the possibility of it being singled out as a bombing target by the Luftwaffe, was heavily camouflaged with brown- and green-coloured netting. However, I have to admit that, when one of my colleagues who joined the RAF and flew over it, was then asked his opinion of the effectiveness of the camouflaging he replied, 'It looks just like a camouflaged Research Station!'

A local unit of the Home Guard, staffed by PO volunteers and led by Captain A.C. Timmis, was set up to protect the Station from sabotage and direct action by enemy agents.

And so the PO ED Research Station, headed by Gorden

Radley, then Director of Research and later Sir Gorden Radley, Director General of the Post Office, went to war – not knowing what the future might bring but determined to 'do its bit'.

Radio Direction Finding

It was suspected that, at the outbreak of war, enemy agents would set up radio beacon transmitters in London to guide bombers to their targets. I was given the task of setting up, as a matter of great urgency, three radio direction-finding stations around London to locate the beacons. With the co-operation of the Ministry of Works and local authorities, and help from the Army, sites were quickly found on high ground at Highgate, Windsor Park and Catford, and equipped with huts and power supplies. The direction-finding loop-aerial receivers I commandeered from the Marconi Co at Chelmsford – they had originally been destined for the Russian Navy. All was in readiness within a month – a revelation compared with the time needed to get similar jobs done in peacetime. But, as an anticlimax, the expected enemy radio beacons in London did not materialise – but if they had, the PO ED was ready for them!

Shore-based radio-direction finding (df) was an important facility used by the Admiralty for keeping watch on the movements of the ships of the German Navy, dating from the First World War. With the outbreak of the Second World War it became urgently necessary to extend the Admiralty network of df stations around the shores of the UK and, where possible, to improve the accuracy. To help in this work the Admiralty sought the help of the Post Office ED – in fact some of the df stations were already located on PO radio-receiving station sites. We, the 'Receiving Group' of the Radio Branch of the ED, had the help of the Government Radio Research Station at Slough which, under the direction of Dr Smith-Rose, was a world authority on radio-direction finding. The RRS had developed the 'Adcock' short-wave direction-finder, which used four vertical aerials over a conducting ground

43

plane to minimise bearing errors arising from wave polarisation. This became the standard design, and its improved accuracy was undoubtedly a factor in winning the surface-ship sea war and in tracking the movements of German submarines attacking the Allied Atlantic convoys.

Beam Bending

By 1940 the air war over the UK had moved on to German bomber attacks, even on cathedral cities such as Coventry. It became clear that the bombers were being guided by radio guidance beams from the Low Countries on the Continent in finding their targets in the UK – the background to which has been told by Professor R.V. Jones in the fascinating book *The Secret War*[4].

The evolution and implementation of the UK counterattack on this radio-beam guidance system became the responsibility of the 80 (Signals) Wing of the Royal Air Force and has been described by Laurie Brettingham in his book *The Beam Benders*[5]. But the innovation of the idea was very much a PO ED concept – notably due to Jim Merriman (later Professor J.H.H. Merriman, CB, FEng, Hon DSc, PO Board Member for Technology). I quote Merriman from Brettingham's book:

'In the early months of 1940 Harold Stanesby (a PO ED colleague) and I began to speculate on ways in which we could manipulate the enemy's radio navigation systems without his knowledge. Our idea was that whenever the enemy set up a radio beacon we might be able to pick up and re-broadcast it on an identical radio-frequency carrier and with identical modulation, but with completely confusing location information.'

The implementation of this technique involved picking up the enemy radio navigation signals at one location in the UK, transmitting them over some miles of coaxial cable to a different location, and then re-transmitting them. The interfer-

44

ence pattern between the original and re-transmitted signals was then sufficient to prevent the air-borne bomber navigator from finding his target.

The design and manufacture of the receiving and transmitting equipment and coaxial cable required for multi-site installation involved a comprehensive and substantial effort from PO ED staff and UK radio industry – as Merriman records:

'Whatever we wanted was available almost before we finished asking for it – it was an interesting phase in one's life. We had clearly defined objectives and almost unlimited powers to command and control.'

The name 'Meacon' was used to describe the PO system – derived from 'Mock' and 'Beacon'. However, soon after its deployment the Germans became aware that their radio navigation system was being thwarted and developed an alternative called 'Knickebein' of greater accuracy and more resistant to counter-measures. The development of counter-measures to this have been described by Professor R.V. Jones and Robert Coburn, Chief Scientist of the Ministry of Defence, in the book *The Secret War*[4].

The Code Breakers

One of the most significant developments in the electronic war – which might well have been a vital factor in bringing the war to a successful conclusion – was the breaking, i.e. the deciphering, of the Enigma code widely used by the Germans for secrecy in their Military and Government line and radio telegraphic communications. These used a version of the International Telegraph (Baudot) Code, in which each letter or numeral is represented by a different combination of five 'on-off' signals. The Enigma machine enabled each combination to be varied as frequently as was needed to ensure a high degree of secrecy.

British deciphering was carried out in conditions of great

secrecy at the Government Communications Headquarters (GCHQ) at Bletchley Park; the full story of this work has only recently (1993) been released. The decoded information, termed 'Ultra', often gave the Allied High Command advance information of great value about the enemy's strategic intentions and movements of his forces when they were in progress. Areas of war thus affected included:

- the 8th Army operations in North Africa and Italy
- submarine warfare on the North Atlantic convoys
- the Allied invasion of Europe

A technological contribution of critical importance to the decoding process, greatly speeding its speed and accuracy, was the creation by a small group of PO Research Branch scientists and engineers at Dollis Hill of an electronic computer called 'Colossus' – the first in the world to embody a 'memory' and a 'stored program' controlling its operation. The term 'Colossus' was not inappropriate since it incorporated some 2,000 valves (this was long before the advent of transistors) and occupied most of a small room.

The Dollis Hill team directly responsible for the creation of 'Colossus' was led by Dr Tom Flowers; it included Dr A.W. Coombs, W.W. Chandler and Sid Broadhurst; the latter brought invaluable knowledge of automatic telephony switching systems. Several other scientists at Dollis Hill contributed to 'Colossus' without knowing it – these included Dr E. Speight, Dr Arnold Lynch and Don Campbell, who developed an optical scanning system. The security surrounding the work on 'Colossus' was so complete that not only they but all others at Dollis Hill – myself included – were totally unaware of the outstanding contribution to the war effort that was in progress.

A 'Freelance' Radio Echo Direction Finding System

The wartime development of radar for the detection and

location of enemy aircraft by pulsed radio waves was carried out under conditions of great secrecy by Robert Watson-Watt and his colleagues from the Government Radio Research Station, Slough, much of the experimental work being done at Bawdsey on the coast of Suffolk and later at the Telecommunication Research Establishment, Malvern[7]. However, such was the secrecy involved that my colleagues and I at the Radio Experimental Branch of the Post Office knew little of this work. Nevertheless, with our 'radio' background, and bearing in mind that we had all been at the receiving end of German bombing, it was not surprising that we also began to consider what could be done to detect aircraft by means of radio.

An interesting lead in was provided by the fact that engineers of the PO, notably Albert Mumford and H.T. Mitchell, had reported in the early 1930s received signal strength fluctuations on a VHF, 6-metre wavelength experimental radio link between Dollis Hill and Colney Heath, Herts, whenever an aircraft flew through the beam between transmitter and receiver.

Not having access to high-power pulsed magnetrons that were the key to the Watson-Watt pulsed radar, my thoughts turned to the possibility of a swept-frequency continuous-wave system on about 500 MHz using triode valves with a power output of some tens of watts, which were then becoming available. Experience with the phase-shifting system incorporated in the PO MUSA suggested a possible means for displaying both bearing and azimuth of an echo simultaneously on a cathode-ray oscilloscope in a readily readable form. With a linear frequency sweep of some tens of MHz, the beat between an echo and the transmitted signal fell in the audio frequencies and was directly proportional to the range. The physical realisation of this concept involved three vertical quarter-wave receiving aerials in an equilateral triangle over a ground plan and a transmitting aerial in the centre. The phase differences between the audio signals derived from the radio signals picked up by the three receiving aerials provided the information enabling the azimuth and elevation bearings to be displayed on the oscilloscope.

With the support of my chiefs Albert Mumford and Capt Charles Booth, a working model was made with the help of colleagues Jim Merriman and Robert White and tried out at Northolt Airbase. The technical details were duly recorded in PO Radio Report No. 789, 1942. But the Watson-Watt pulse-modulated radar was by then being deployed on a large scale and there was no effort available to pursue another system. And so the further development of this 'freelance' PO contribution had of necessity to be put on one side.

The Moon as the First Communication Satellite

Sitting in an armchair on the lawn at home in that summer of 1940, when the fate of Britain – and perhaps the Western world – was being decided by a few courageous RAF pilots in their Spitfires and Hurricanes, I began to consider the possibility of using the Moon as a passive communication satellite by beaming radio waves at its surface and picking up the scattered waves at any other location on Earth from which the Moon was visible. It might thus serve as a means of telegraph or telephone communication – for example, of encoded signals for military purposes.

Calculations showed that, with microwave powers of about 1 kW and dish aerials some 3 metres in diameter, the radiated energy could be concentrated in a beam about 0.5 degree wide that could illuminate the Moon at a distance of 250,000 miles and produce a scattered signal energy at the receiver adequate for a telephone channel of usable quality. However, the two-way transmission delay due to the finite velocity of radio waves, 186,000 miles per second, was about 2.5 seconds – unimportant for telegraph communication but a handicap for normal telephone conversation.

However, my memorandum on this received short shrift from high quarters in the PO – 'What is all this Moonshine?' 'Did I not realise there was a war on?' It was with some satisfaction that I learned later, from Sir Edward Appleton's lecture on 'The Scientific Principles of Radiolocation' at the

Institution of Electrical Engineers in 1946, that engineers of the US Army Signal Corps at Fort Monmouth, USA, had detected radio echoes from the Moon in 1945, albeit on a longer wavelength than I had envisaged. And in 1959 the Bell Telephone Laboratories scientists bounced signals off the Moon as a preliminary to tests with their balloon satellite Echo.

5

Microwave Radio Communication

The war years had given a powerful impetus to the use of microwaves, i.e. radio waves with wavelengths between 3 and 30 centimetres (30 GHz to 3 GHz frequency) for radar. This had resulted in the development of klystron and magnetron oscillators for the generation of microwaves, waveguides and aerials for transmission and crystal detectors for reception. These devices provided a valuable technological background for the development of microwave radio-relay systems for inter-city multi-channel telephony and television transmission via hilltop sites – often an economic and more rapidly provided alternative to coaxial cables laid in the ground. (See plates 8 and 9) The American Telephone and Telegraph Company and the Bell Telephone Laboratories, the British Post Office ED and its Radio Experimental Branch were quick to realise the potential of the new technique and put in hand research and development work. The PO ED contribution was carried out in collaboration with the UK telecommunications industry, notably with Standard Telecommunication Laboratories and the General Electric Company. A more detailed account of these developments has been given in Chapter 11 of *The Communications Miracle*[1] and in *Memoirs of a Telecommunications Engineer*[3].

Microwave Research at the PO ED Radio Experimental Branch, Dollis Hill

For my part I welcomed this extension of the work of the

Radio Experimental Branch at Dollis Hill in the immediate postwar years – it seemed logically right to be moving up the radio frequency spectrum from the 3 to 10 MHz of short-wave (metric) radio waves to the 3 to 30 GHz of (centimetric) microwaves! And how wise, and perhaps perceptive, was Heinrich Hertz in the 1880s when his historic discovery of radio waves was made on centimetric wavelengths, using compact dipole aerials and parabolic reflectors. It also seems fitting that these are now called 'Hertzian' waves.

Certain aspects of the work at Dollis Hill can now be seen as particularly significant:

- the statistical study of the propagation of microwaves on overland and sea paths
- the use of frequency modulation of the microwave carrier
- the pioneering use of the travelling-wave tube as a microwave amplifier

The propagation studies were vital for the economic design of radio-relay systems to achieve the overall signal-to-noise standards of performance required for multi-channel telephony and television. Microwaves are subject to fading under conditions of varying atmospheric refraction, e.g. due to fog and multi-path transmission from ground-reflected waves. Radio-relay system design requires such information in statistical form to determine the transmitter power, aerial gain and height above ground necessary to achieve the required overall performance standards.

The use of frequency modulation for multi-channel telephony, as compared with amplitude modulation employed on earlier PO radio-relay systems, was pioneered by J.H.H. Merriman and R.W. White on a VHF radio link between Douglas in the Isle of Man and Holyhead on the mainland in order to combat high levels of noise arising from power line interference. Frequency modulation, invented by Armstrong in the USA for use in VHF/UHF television broadcasting, became the preferred modulation technique for multi-channel

51

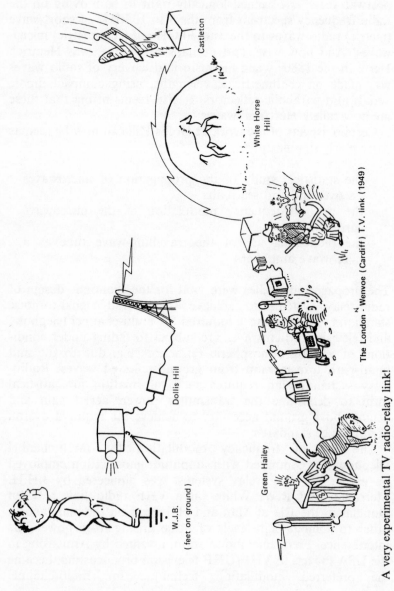

A very experimental TV radio-relay link!

The London - Wenvoe (Cardiff) T.V. link (1949)

Castleton

White Horse Hill

Dollis Hill

W.J.B.
(feet on ground)

Green Hailey

52

telephony and television radio-relay systems. It offered improved signal-to-noise ratio and freedom from distortion due to amplitude non-linearity, as compared with amplitude modulation. However, there remained a problem due to phase non-linearity in the transmission path which caused crosstalk between telephone channels. My modest contribution was to devise a theory which enabled such crosstalk to be minimised.

Until the end of the war in 1945 there was no commercially available microwave amplifier. However, an Austrian named Rudolf Kompfner, whose earlier training had been as an architect, was working in the Clarendon Laboratory, Cambridge University, on a low-noise microwave amplifier to precede the crystal frequency-changer first stage of radar receivers, with the aim of increasing the radar range. Kompfner's device used an electron beam passing through the centre of a wire helix at the beginning of which a microwave signal could be launched and at the end an amplified signal abstracted. His first success came in 1942 when he noted that his travelling-wave tube was 'a completely untuned amplifier'.

Meanwhile the Bell Laboratories had pursued the development of a 4GHz triode amplifier for their TD2 microwave radio-relay system – with its incredibly small cathode-grid-anode spacing, this was a real tour-de-force to manufacture. The amplifier also depended on critically tuned circuits to produce gain.

I met Rudolf Kompfner on the wartime Admiralty-sponsored Co-ordination of Valve Development Committee (CVD). Realising that a travelling-wave tube amplifier would be easier to manufacture than a triode, could work at higher frequencies than 4GHz and was essentially wideband, I persuaded the CVD to finance the development of a microwave travelling wave-tube amplifier, based on Kompfner's experimental work. The outcome was a highly successful device, developed by D.C. Rogers of Standard Telecommunication Laboratories and used on the Post Office Manchester–Kirk O'Shotts radio-relay system – the first in the world to use travelling-wave tubes commercially (1952). With this lead, travelling-wave tubes were later widely used by other telecom-

53

munication organisations, including the Bell Laboratories 6GHz TH and 11GHz TL radio-relay systems; they have also been used in satellite communication systems.

The International Standardisation of Microwave Radio-relay Systems

As the use of microwave radio-relay systems for inter-city telephone communication and television signal distribution in Europe and America expanded in the 1950s and 1960s, it became apparent that there was a need for standardisation of the basic technical parameters in order to facilitate the setting-up of systems that crossed national boundaries and to maintain the transmission quality on long-distance connections.

The work of arriving at internationally accepted standards was carried out by the International Radio, and Telephone and Telegraph Consultative Committees (CCIR and CCITT) of the International Telecommunication Union (ITU), an organ of the United Nations with headquarters in Geneva. Remarkably, in spite of the 'cold war' and 'iron curtain' situation that then existed, the USSR and the Warsaw Pact countries participated without major problems in the work of these Committees – perhaps because it gave them a window on Western technological development!

The technical standards arrived at by the CCIR and CCITT were not mandatory, they were expressed as 'Recommendations' in response to carefully formulated technical 'Questions' that always began with the phrase 'Recognising that...'. Even so, the standards served a valuable purpose in guiding the development of equipment in the participating countries, as well as the setting-up of links that crossed national boundaries.

Proposals for the 'Recommendations' were prepared by International 'Study Groups', with representatives mainly from those countries most actively involved in system development and approved at Plenary Sessions of the ITU that met every few years. In the UK the preparatory work at national level

54

was carried out by the British Post Office Engineering Department.

It was through working on one of these preparatory national committees in the early 1950s, mainly in helping to produce draft 'Recommendations', that I first became familiar with the organisation and objectives of the CCIR. This eventually led to participation in CCIR International Study Group meetings in Geneva, and elsewhere in Europe, the United States and Japan, where they were generally hosted by the Post, Telephone and Telegraph (PTT) Administration of the country concerned.

This experience I found to be highly educative – not only because of the need effectively to debate technical points with national and international telecommunication experts, but also because it often required one to defend an agreed national position at the International Study Group level, which sometimes involved reaching acceptable compromises. Following a PO colleague (Harold Stanesby), I became International Chairman of CCIR Study Group IX (Radio-Relay Systems) in 1957 – I was then with PO ED Inland Radio Branch – with responsibility for presenting, and securing formal approval of draft 'Recommendations' at the CCIR Plenary Sessions in Los Angeles (1959) and Geneva (1963).

It is with some pride that I can record that by 1963 international agreement had been reached on all the basic technical characteristics of multi-channel frequency-division multiplex telephone, and television, microwave radio-relay systems, enshrined in the documents of the CCIR and which later I summarised in a paper for the Institution of Electrical Engineers, London[8].

An enjoyable aspect of this work was the friendships it created – often enhanced by the joys of international travel! I remember in particular G. Dawson, B.B. Jacobson and L.J.I. Nickels of Standard Telecommunication Laboratories, and G. Griffiths of the General Electric Company, who were part of the UK team led by my chief Capt C.F. Booth. L.J.I. Nickels, with his excellent command of the French language, was especially helpful in document preparation and ensuring that the French and English texts meant the same thing! And it was a pleasure to work with Rene Sueur of the Centre Nationale d'Études des Télécommunications (CNET) in France, Ed Bemis of the American Telephone and Telegraph Company and Dr Dietrich of the German Bundespost, whose co-operation was both effective and friendly.

First Microwave Links Across the English Channel

The first microwave link across the English Channel was an experimental one, set up in 1930 by Standard Telephones and Cables, UK and their French partners Le Materiel Téléphonique between Lympne, near Dover and St Engleverte, Pas de Calais. This very early experiment, which used parabolic reflector transmitting and receiving aerials, was interesting in that it demonstrated received signal level variations due to a sea-reflected wave as the tide rose and fell.

To the BBC must go the honour of achieving, in 1952, the first television microwave link across the Channel, using OB (outside broadcast) equipment between Dover and Calais. The fact that this carried the first-ever live television pictures between Europe and the UK made a considerable impression on the viewing public and created a strong impetus towards the creation of a European television distribution network.

The growth of telephone communication with the Continent in the 1950s, and the need for a permanent television link, led to an agreement between the French PTT and the British PO to establish a microwave link across the English Channel between Tolsford Hill, near Folkstone, and Fiennes on the Pas de Calais – commissioned in 1959. The then newly established technical standards evolved by CCIR Study Group IX provided a basis for this link; the equipment was provided jointly by STC (UK) for the multi-channel telephony component and LMT (France) for the television component. It is noteworthy that the technical design corrected for the sea-reflected wave was first observed in 1930.

Ongoing Microwave System Development in the UK

From this English Channel beginning, microwave radio-relay provision in the UK for inter-city trunk telephone circuits and for the growing need for television distribution to regional transmitters proceeded apace. By the 1980s a comprehensive national radio-relay network had been established, complementing the multi-channel telephone and television cable network, and with its focal point at the Post Office (now British Telecom) Tower in London, opened by the Prime Minister, Harold Wilson, in 1965.

Not only did these microwave developments in the 1950s and later years create an important means for improving terrestrial communications and provide an important profit earner for the UK telecommunications industry, but they also evolved a vital technical know-how basis for the worldwide satellite communication system that was to follow.

6

A Commonwealth Fund Fellowship in the USA
1955–56

In 1955 it was my good fortune to be awarded a Commonwealth Fund Fellowship for 'advanced studies and travel' in the USA – a sabbatical year from the Post Office that turned out to be both enjoyable and rewarding.

The CFF is an American philanthropic foundation that was set up in 1925 by Mr and Mrs Ed Harkness, who had made a substantial fortune from Standard Oil of America. The income from the Foundation's original endowment of $100 million was used to finance medical research and advanced educational projects in the USA, and to endow some 25 British Fellowships, several others in Australia and New Zealand, and a few in European countries. Of the British Fellowships five were allotted to the Civil Service, of which mine was one.

The aims of the Fellowships at that time were to promote a better understanding of, and co-operation with, the USA by professional men and women in overseas countries who might become leaders and influence opinion in those countries. However, the objectives of the Foundation have been modified in recent years to put more emphasis on medical research and social studies within the USA.

The CFF awards were made in general to university graduates who had already embarked on a profession, typically in science, engineering, journalism, literature, medicine or business studies. Notable UK awards in past years had been to Sir William Penney ('father' of the British atom bomb, known as the 'Penney Banger'!), Alistair Cooke, whose broadcasts to the UK made him a most effective publicist for the USA, and the writer Eric Linklater, whose book *Juan in America* was based on his CFF travels in the USA.

The programme of studies I had proposed to the CFF covered aspects of telecommunications ranging from research and development in microwave radio and mobile radio systems, to operational, administrative and regulatory aspects. This the CFF Director Lansing Hammond readily agreed to and left me free to make my own detailed arrangements for visits to appropriate organisations, firms and universities. The UK Embassy in Washington, in the person of Colonel Reid, the Telecommunications Attaché was helpful in establishing contacts, as was Ed Bemis of the American Telephone and Telegraph Co, whom I knew well from our work on CCIR Study Group IX.

I sailed to New York from Southampton in the French liner *Liberté* in September 1955 in company with three other CFF fellows – a voyage memorable for an encounter with Hurricane Hazel of that year, which left the skyscrapers in New York swaying for a day or two after our arrival! Ed Bemis had arranged for me to lodge with a pleasant American family in Summit, New Jersey, not far from the Bell Laboratories at Murray Hill, NJ – which became my base of operations for the next six months in the USA. Summit proved to be a good choice, for it led to friendships with scientists and engineers from the Bell Laboratories who lived there, and it was distinctly 'anglophile', having a cinema that specialised in British films!

The first few weeks after my arrival were spent with ATT at its 463 West Street, New York, headquarters, studying the organisation of that company and the planning of the micro-wave radio-relay systems that had become essential to its Long-Lines operation to meet the urgent demand for distribution of television programmes throughout the United States. A pleasant feature of my daily journey from Summit was the ferry trip across the Hudson river, from the Lackawanna Rail Terminal, New Jersey, to West Street, NY and its backdrop of skyscrapers and the Empire State Tower. It was on this ferry that J.S. Black of ATT/Bell had originated, and scribbled on paper, the all-important invention of 'negative feedback' in amplifiers that became essential in the design of long land and submarine telephone cable systems.

Then followed a period with the Bell Laboratories, initially at Murray Hill, where I met Dr J.S. Pierce, who was then working on travelling-wave tube design for microwave radio-relay systems – that is when not engaged in his hobby of science-fiction writing or thinking up ideas for communication by satellites!

A visit to the Bell Laboratory at Holmdel, NJ, brought an inspiring contact with Dr H.T. Friis who, with his colleagues at Holmdel, was responsible for much of the research that provided the basis for the Bell TD2 and later microwave radio-relay systems. In the 1950s and 1960s Holmdel was essentially a field laboratory, with a staff of a hundred or so housed in single-storey wooden huts – today it comprises air-conditioned multi-storey buildings housing thousands of staff. I remember discussing with Friis the ideal number of staff for a research laboratory – he said, after some thought, 'Perhaps a hundred – I could then choose them individually.' Research at Holmdel was by no means abstract – on a blackboard in one of the laboratories I noticed, superimposed on a background of mathematical equations and triple integrals, the stern injunction 'dollars per message channel per mile' – it appeared that Dr Kelly, then Deputy Head of the Bell Laboratories, had the previous day visited Holmdel and reminded his research staff of their prime objective!

The study programme during the first six months of my Fellowship included the following visits:

American Telephone and Telegraph Co, New York (company organisation and long-lines planning)

Bell Telephone Laboratories, Murray Hill and Holmdel, NJ (microwave radio-relay and waveguide systems)

Federal Telecommunications Laboratories, Nutley, NJ (tropospheric-scatter radio-relay systems)

National Bureau of Standards, Boulder, Colorado (radio-wave propagation studies)

Radio Corporation of America, Princeton, NJ (colour television systems)
Federal Communications Commission, Washington, DC (regulatory and licensing aspects of radio systems)

In return for paying my salary during the sabbatical year I wrote several reports for the Post Office, mostly on technical matters and a few on staff management in the Bell Laboratories, e.g. procedures for career planning and salary determination. In retrospect, and in comparison with today's highly competitive atmosphere, which inhibits the free flow of information between companies, it seems remarkable how free I was to visit and discuss technical matters, not only in Bell but also in other organisations.

After the first period of technical studies, based mainly on the East Coast, the CFF expected the Fellows to travel widely in the USA, visiting universities and other relevant organisations, but which also enabled one to see the countryside and meet people in the various States. And, most generously, the CFF paid for one's wife to accompany the Fellow on his travels. By now I had acquired a secondhand DeSoto car, and together Margaret and I travelled some 12,000 miles around the USA during three months beginning in June 1956. We started in Summit, New Jersey, travelled south to Florida, along the Gulf Coast and through Texas and Arizona, over the Coastal Range of Mountains to San Diego, up the Pacific Coast to San Francisco, and then eastwards over the Rocky Mountains and Yellowstone Park, through the Midwest states to New York State and eventually back to Summit, NJ. It was an interesting experience to travel from spring weather in New Jersey to summer in Florida, and later to encounter winter and snow-clad roads in the Rockies, but finally to catch up with summer in New Jersey.

We lived mainly in motels, which were comfortable and inexpensive, and of course 'gas' in the USA was much cheaper than petrol in the UK. My diary records that our average daily expenditure was $14, then about £7 – no doubt helped by generous hospitality from ATT/Bell people, universities and firms.

From a personal point of view the Fellowship was most rewarding and enjoyable, bringing many new friends and of course a greatly enhanced picture of the United States and knowledge of its people. Professionally it gave me a much broader outlook on the telecommunications industry, and in particular a preview of the kind of developments and problems that the UK would be faced with in this field. The contacts and friendships that I made with ATT/Bell people were later to prove of considerable value in the development of joint USA/ UK projects such as satellite communications and transatlantic submarine cable systems that followed in the next decade.

7

The Post Office and Television

The pioneering work of John Logie Baird and the splendid commercial initiatives of Electric and Musical Industries (EMI) and the Marconi Company which enabled the BBC to set up the world's first public television service in 1936 I have described elsewhere[1].

The television service from Alexandra Palace in London had to be shut down with the outbreak of war in 1939, because of the risk that the transmitter might serve as a beacon for German bombers. Appropriately enough, this was in the middle of a Mickey Mouse cartoon with Mickey saying, '...I t'ink I go home!'

Soon after the end of the war the BBC television transmissions from Alexandra Palace were resumed, after a titanic battle between the mechanically-scanned Baird system and the electronically-scanned Zworykin system of EMI-Marconi.

This chapter marks a pause in the account of my professional life to review briefly the many and varied contributions of the Post Office, through its Administrative and Engineering Departments, to the development of television broadcasting in the United Kingdom from the 1930s to 1960s, when it became first a Public Corporation (1969) and later British Telecom[9].

The Post Office was then a Government department under the control of a Postmaster General, responsible to Parliament for the postal, telephone and telegraph services under the Telegraph Act of 1868; this was extended by the Wireless Telegraphy Act of 1904 to include all wireless stations, and by the Wireless Telegraphy Act of 1949 to include the regulation of television broadcasting. This involved the radio frequencies

63

and transmission standards to be used, and protection of the quality of service to viewers. The Television Advisory Committee, set up in 1945 with representatives of the BBC, the radio industry and the PO, advised on planning the service, in particular with regard to the standards to be adopted, both in the UK and internationally.

In view of its role as the Government Department responsible for regulation of the use of the radio frequency spectrum, the Radio and Research Branches of the PO Engineering Department carried out extensive studies in several key areas, including:

- wave propagation studies to determine service coverage areas and avoid interference between transmitters sharing the same radio frequency channel
- the technical characteristics of the transmitted television signal waveform to ensure good quality pictures together with efficient use of the radio spectrum and economic transmission over cable and radio-relay links

Post Office responsibilities included the leading, and co-ordination of the work of UK delegations with representatives of the Broadcasting Authority, Radio Industry, Scientific and Operating Agencies, and its own experts, in the standardisation of the technical characteristics of television broadcasting and transmission systems via the Radio (CCIR) and Telephone and Telegraph (CCITT) Consultative Committees of the International Telecommunication Union (ITU). The overall aims of this work were to facilitate television programme exchanges between members of the ITU and to protect the quality of service to television viewers.

In addition to this committee work and supporting studies, the PO ED was actively involved in providing the inter-city links by coaxial cable and microwave radio-relay needed to feed the expanding network of BBC, and later ITV, regional television transmitting stations. In this work it had to learn to cope with the subtle 'phase-frequency' characteristics of video channels, as compared with 'amplitude-frequency' characteristics that were all that were needed for multi-channel telephone systems, and which determined the video waveform response of a transmission path. A member of the PO ED Research Branch, Dr N.W. Lewis, with W.E. Thomson and J.W. Allnatt, devised a method for defining and testing the waveform response of video channels, known as the 'K' factor, which could be related to the subjective impairment of picture quality caused by waveform distortion – a technique that was adopted internationally by the CCIR and widely used. In co-operation with the BBC, they also carried out extensive subjective tests on the impairment of picture quality that could arise from noise and interference. The definition of acceptable levels of noise and interference was essential for the economic design and the practical planning of television broadcasting and transmission systems. The excellent picture quality enjoyed by today's television viewers owes much to the work of Dr Lewis and his colleagues[9].

To meet the requirements of the 1949 Wireless Telegraphy Act, the Post Office ED operated a service for the detection and suppression of radio-interference to television and sound radio reception caused by car ignition systems, electrical machinery and power lines. With the UK Electrical Research Association the Radio Branch of the ED developed radio-interference measuring equipment that was eventually standardised internationally via the CISPR (ITU International Special Committee for Radio Interference).

The PO was also responsible for the licensing of radio transmitters and receivers and operated a direction-finding service for the location of unlicensed transmitters. But with the growth of television broadcasting in the 1940s and the broadcasters' dependence on income from the TV licence fee, a real problem arose from the increasing number of 'TV pirates' who watched programmes without a licence. This was of some concern to the Postmaster General, Earl de la Warr, who had been challenged in the House of Commons to find a solution for the detection of the 'pirates'. (See plates 10 and 11)

I was then in the Radio Experimental Branch at Dollis Hill, where the PMG had come looking for a solution, and happily was able to offer one. This took the form of a loop-aerial and a radio receiver tuned to a harmonic of the induction magnetic field created by the 10 kHz saw-tooth current in the line-scanning coils of a working television receiver. Thus was born in 1952 the first 'TV detection van'; equipped with three loop aerials on the roof, it could locate a working TV receiver as being in front or behind, to right or left, of the van position. The mere sight of the van in an area infested by 'pirates' was sufficient to send them hurrying to pay for their licences – I only wish I had been able to collect a mere 5 percent of the additional licence revenue thus created!

W.J.B. chasing TV pirates! (1952)

8

The Inland Radio Branch PO ED HQ 1954–60

With my promotion to Head of Branch in 1954 came a move from Dollis Hill to the Radio Branch of the PO Engineering Department Headquarters in Armour House, St Martins-le-Grand, London, not far from St Paul's Cathedral. Across the road from Armour House was the PO Administration HQ building which contained the offices of the Postmaster General, with his top-hatted and liveried attendants, and the Director General of the Post Office, with his Deputies and Departments.

My first reactions to this move were somewhat mixed. I knew I would miss the experimental work, the 'hands-on' contact with equipment, and discussions with like-minded colleagues at Dollis Hill. On the other hand, the move to Engineering Department Headquarters opened the door to a

W.J.B. bound for the city! (1954)

much wider experience of the Post Office and the economic and political realities that governed its functioning. It also led to a better understanding of the Telecommunications Industry in the UK and how its resources could be used to provide, in co-operation with the PO, improved and more cost-effective communication services to the public.

The work of the ED Radio Branch at that time covered the following main areas of responsibility:

- the planning and provision of the inland microwave radio-relay trunk network, in co-operation with the ED Lines Branch and the Inland Telecommunication Department (ITD) of the Administration
- the engineering aspects of inland and maritime mobile VHF radio systems and the planning of frequency allocations in co-operation with ITD and the Inspectorate of Wireless Telegraphy
- the engineering aspects involved in the regulation of broadcasting and the control of radio interference, including frequency allocations and coverage areas for the broadcast services
- participation in the work of the International Radio Consultative Committee (CCIR) via the UK and International Study Groups, notably Study Group IX Microwave Radio-Relay Systems) and Study Group XI (Television)

This broader area of responsibility was quite challenging, however I had very supportive and capable colleagues who were quick to tell me when I was 'putting a foot wrong' – and overall it was a very educative period of my professional career.

My *Memoirs*[3] give an account in some detail of the work involved and its problems, but perhaps a few aspects are worth recalling here.

Because the PO was under strict Treasury control the provision of microwave radio-relay systems had to be authorised on a 'link by link' basis whenever the BBC required a feed to each regional television transmitter. This was complicated by a degree of rivalry between the 'Radio' and the 'Lines' Branches of the ED – the latter had a bias towards the well-tried, buried-in-the-ground coaxial cable technology, developed primarily for multi-channel intercity trunk telephony but which was not readily adaptable to television. Microwave radio-relay, on the other hand, was immediately suitable for television, and could often be provided more quickly and cheaply than cable. This situation at first inhibited the provision of a nationwide microwave radio-relay network, with integrated provision for television and multi-channel telephony and built-in provision for growth.

In the United States the spread of television broadcasting from the 1940s onwards, under the drive of advertising-sponsored organisations such as the Columbia Broadcasting System (CBS) and the Radio Corporation of America (RCA), created an urgent demand for a nationwide video network to enable hundreds of broadcasting stations to transmit simultaneously the same programmes and advertisements. This need was met initially by the American Telephone and Telegraph Co's TD2 microwave radio-relay system, evolved from the Bell Laboratories research described in Part 2, Chapter 5.

For the reasons described above the British Post Office was slower to plan and develop an integrated television and multi-channel telephony network, but this was eventually accomplished with the aid of equipment supplied by Standard Telephones and Cables, the General Electric Co and the Marconi Company. The national network had its focal point in the Post Office Tower, which was once described, at an Institution of Electrical Engineers dinner, as 'that splendid phallic emblem, a monument to the virility of the Engineer-in-Chief of the Post Office!'

Another activity, which I found particularly interesting in view of my sailing hobby, was to participate in the work of an historic International Maritime Conference at The Hague in 1957. This was set up under the auspices of the CCIR and the International Radio Maritime Committee (CIRM) of the ITU to allocate frequency channels and operational procedures for the various maritime services, including distress and calling, port operations, ship-to-ship and ship-to-shore telephony, and coastguards. These were of course vital for commercial maritime services, but even amateur sailors such as myself found them valuable in dealing with the hazards of the ocean, and not least being able to call for help when it was most needed.

But by the 1960s another development in the field of radio was taking place that was to transform world communications, and which led to the most exciting and rewarding phase of my professional career – the beginning of worldwide communication by earth-orbiting satellites.

9

The Beginning of Satellite Communications:
Space Communication Systems Branch
PO ED HQ 1961–63

History

The story of the beginning of satellite communications has been told in some detail in *The Communications Miracle* and *Memoirs of a Telecommunications Engineer* – suffice it to recall here the key events that began this epoch-making event in world communications.

The most significant was an article by the noted British science-fiction writer A.C. Clarke in the journal *Wireless World* in 1945 entitled 'Extra-Terrestrial Relays – Can Rocket Stations Give World-wide Coverage?' Clarke's proposal envisaged three satellites spaced apart in a west-to-east equatorial orbit around the Earth at a height of 22,300 miles – at which height each would appear stationary relative to an observer on the ground. This proposal – which contained all the basic features of present-day satellite systems – was made some 12 years before the first satellite was launched. As Clarke has said, 'it went down like a lead balloon' and received very little attention at the time[10].

Meanwhile another science-fiction writer, Dr J.R. Pierce, a scientist working on communication problems in the Bell Telephone Laboratories, USA, had written an article 'Orbital Radio Relays' in the magazine *Jet Propulsion* in 1955 which discussed the possibilities of 'passive' satellites, i.e. reflectors of

71

EXTRA-TERRESTRIAL RELAYS

Can Rocket Stations
Give World-wide Radio Coverage?

By ARTHUR C. CLARKE

ALTHOUGH it is possible, by a suitable choice of frequencies and routes, to provide telephony circuits between any two points or regions of the earth for a large part of the time, long-distance communication is greatly hampered by the peculiarities of the ionosphere, and there are even occasions when it may be impossible. A true broadcast service, giving constant field strength at all times over the whole globe would be invaluable, not to say indispensable, in a world society.

Unsatisfactory though the telephony and telegraph position is, that of television is far worse, since ionospheric transmission cannot be employed at all. The service area of a television station, even on a very good site, is only about a hundred miles across. To cover a small country such as Great Britain would require a network of transmitters, connected by coaxial lines, waveguides or VHF relay links. A recent theoretical study[1] has shown that such a system would require repeaters at intervals of fifty miles or less. A system of this kind could provide television coverage, at a very considerable cost, over the whole of a small country. It would be out of the question to provide a large continent with such a service, and only the main centres of population could be included in the network.

The problem is equally serious when an attempt is made to link television services in different parts of the globe. A relay chain several thousand miles long would cost millions, and transoceanic services would still be impossible. Similar considerations apply to the provision of wide-band frequency modulation and other services, such as high-speed facsimile which are by their nature restricted to the ultra-high-frequencies.

Many may consider the solution proposed in this discussion too far-fetched to be taken very seriously. Such an attitude is unreasonable, as everything envisaged here is a logical extension of developments in the last ten years—in particular the perfection of the long-range rocket of which V2 was the prototype. While this article was being written, it was announced that the Germans were considering a similar project, which they believed possible within fifty to a hundred years.

(*Reprinted from* JET PROPULSION, *April, 1955*)

Orbital Radio Relays

J. R. PIERCE[1]

Bell Telephone Laboratories, Murray Hill, N. J.

While orbital radio relays probably could not compete with microwave radio relay for communication over land, they might be useful in transoceanic communication. Three sorts of repeaters appear to be consistent with microwave art: (a) 100-ft reflecting spheres at an altitude of around 2200 miles; (b) a 100-ft oriented plane mirror in a 24-hr orbit, at an altitude of 22,000 miles; (c) an active repeater in a 24-hr orbit. Cases (a) and (b) require at 10-cm wavelength 250-ft-diam antennas and 100-kw and 50-kw power, respectively; in case (c), using 250-ft antennas on the ground and 10-ft antennas on the repeater; only 100 watts on the ground and 0.03 watt on the repeater would be required; in this case one should probably use smaller antennas on the ground. In cases (b) and (c) the problem of maintaining the correct orientation and position of the repeater is critical; perturbations by the moon and sun might cause the satellite to rock or wander prohibitively.

radio waves, and 'active' satellites carrying radio receiving and transmitting equipment powered by the Sun.[11][12]

But it was not until 1957, when the USSR launched a grapefruit-size satellite Sputnik I in a low Earth orbit, which carried a VHF radio transmitter that could be heard over most of the world, that communication scientists and engineers – especially in the USA – woke up to the fact that satellites 'were for real'.

In 1960 J.R. Pierce and R. Kompfner at Bell Laboratories launched their 100ft diameter balloon satellite ECHO I in a 1000-mile-high Earth orbit. Made of metallic film, it reflected microwave radio waves beamed at it, albeit with strength to provide only a single voice channel. But because it was readily visible to the naked eye as a glowing orb, especially at sunrise and sundown, it provided a convincing demonstration for all to see of the reality of satellites.

These events were not lost on the Post Office engineers, especially those with a background of radio, who saw the potential of satellites for providing economically long-distance telephone and television communication, by-passing conventional land and sea cables.

And so it was in 1961 that the PO ED, under the leadership of its Chief Engineer, Sir Albert Mumford, set up its first 'Space Communication Systems' Branch in Armour House, St Martins-le-Grand, London. However, I have a feeling that the conservative PO Administration on the other side of St Martins-le-Grand thought that this was all 'a bit of science fiction' and wondered what the engineers were landing them in!

The PO ED Space Communication Systems Branch

It was with much pride, and a feeling of excitement at the challenge of things to come, that I was appointed Head of the new Space Communication Systems Branch in 1961, supported by a hand-picked team, some with knowledge of microwave radio techniques drawn from the Inland Radio Branch. The basic remit of the Space Communication Systems Branch was to study all aspects of satellite system design in order to assess

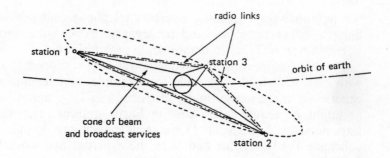

Three satellite stations would ensure complete coverage of the globe.

(a) A.C. Clarke's (1945) satellite system proposal 3 satellites in 24-hour synchronous orbit at 22,300 miles height: transmission delay 0.3 second.

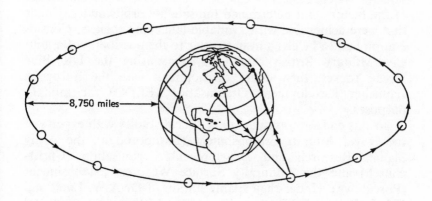

(b) Proposal made at IEE International Conference on Satellite Communication, London (1962) (12 satellites in 8-hour sub-synchronous orbit at 8,750 miles height: transmission delay 0.13 second)

Synchronous and sub-synchronous satellite orbits

75

the potential for providing overseas telephone and television links to other countries, and to organise the construction of Earth station facilities to demonstrate practicability.

The PO Engineering Department was well equipped to deal with this new field – it had, for example, civil engineering experience in the design and construction of large aerials such as might be required for satellite Earth stations. The Radio Experimental Branch at Dollis Hill under my friend and colleague F.J.D. Taylor had both the expertise and workshop facilities to design and construct receiving and transmitting equipment, whilst the Research Branch at Dollis Hill could provide computer expertise such as might be involved in satellite tracking. And earlier work on microwave radio-relay systems provided knowledge of UK Government and Industry research facilities that might be useful in specialised areas such as low-noise microwave amplifiers and high-power microwave transmitters.

In addition to its studies of the communication aspects of satellite systems, the PO ED needed to have some knowledge of the factors that determined the satellite orbits and payloads that were achievable with available launching rockets. Consideration had to be given in particular to the possibility of a joint Civil/Military British satellite system, using the UK Blue Streak rocket, then under development with the European Launcher Development Organisation (ELDO) for military purposes.

To this end we took part in technical studies with experts of the Royal Aircraft Establishment (Farnborough), the Army Signals Research and Development Organisation (Christchurch) and the Admiralty Surface Weapons Establishment (Portsdown). Under the capable tuition of Dr A.W. Lines and E.G.C. Burt at RAE, my colleagues and I learned a good deal about orbits, satellite payloads and rockets. However, for a variety of economic, technical and political reasons the proposal to develop the UK Blue Streak rocket for satellite launching did not mature, and it was the Americans who eventually entered this field via the US National Aeronautics and Space Administration (NASA).[13]

In 1962 a British Commonwealth Conference on Satellite Communications explored various organisational possibilities, e.g for a world system, a Commonwealth/European system or participation in an American system. In the event no firm decision was made, except to support UK participation in tests with the Telstar (ATT) and Relay (NASA) satellites later that year.

A Joint Civil–Military Satellite Mission to the USA 1960

Under the aegis of the UK Cabinet Office the Post Office sent in 1960 a Joint Civil–Military Mission to the USA to investigate at first hand satellite and space system developments in that country, notably at NASA establishments on the West Coast. The Civil team was led by my chief, Capt C.F. Booth, and included myself and F.J.D. Taylor.

The outcome was an agreement, signed with NASA in February 1961, of far-reaching importance for the UK. It stated that the Post Office would take part in satellite communication tests across the North Atlantic, and would build a satellite Earth station for this purpose at its own expense.

And so began the most exciting and challenging period of my professional life, involving a project with many new and untried technical aspects and a large civil engineering component, that had to be completed on a virgin site within a period of two years – with most of the world watching the outcome on television!

The Telstar and Relay Satellite Projects

The Telstar Satellite Project was created and funded by the American Telephone and Telegraph Company and the Bell Laboratories as a private venture, aimed at maintaining their pre-eminence in long-distance communications. In parallel with the Telstar project, and leaning heavily on it for technical guidance in the communication design aspects, NASA sponsored a similar Relay project, with the Radio Corporation of America as the prime contractor. NASA provided satellite launching facilities at Cape Canaveral and satellite tracking facilities at its Goddard Space Flight Centre for both projects.

The objectives of both projects were similar – to demonstrate that active communication satellites could provide reliable, good-quality long-distance telephone, telegraph, data, facsimile and television transmission, and collect scientific data about the space environment to aid in the development of future generations of satellites.

The Telstar satellite was launched from Cape Canaveral on 10 July 1962 in a west-to-east elliptical orbit, the height ranging from 390 to 3,500 miles. This was a long way short of the 'stationary', 24-hour period, Equatorial orbit at 22,300 miles height envisaged by Clarke – it was dictated primarily by the rocket power then available to put a 170 lb payload into orbit. The period of the Telstar orbit was 2.5 hours, and the time during which it was simultaneously 'visible' on both sides of the Atlantic was about one hour, during which the narrow beamwidth Earth station aerials had to track it accurately.

The plane of the orbit was inclined at about 45 degrees to the Equator, an inclination chosen to provide information about possible damage to the electronic components that might arise from radiation in space or micro-meteorites. The satellite was nearly spherical, 34.5 inches in diameter, and weighed 170 lbs. It was 'spin stabilised' to maintain the axis direction in space, controlled from the Earth by gas jets on the satellite via a telemetry radio link.

The communications repeater on the satellite received signals from the Earth stations at 6 GHz and transmitted them at 4 GHz with an output power of 2 watts from a travelling-wave tube amplifier. It provided a bandwidth of 50 MHz, accommodating a frequency-modulated carrier bearing 600 frequency-division multiplex telephone channels or a television signal. Electrical power was provided from the Sun's rays by solar cells on the satellite's surface, and storage batteries when the satellite was in the Earth's shadow.

78

Three Earth stations co-operated in the transatlantic Telstar/ Relay projects:

- the ATT/Bell station at Andover, Maine, USA, with a large 170 ft-long steerable horn aerial, inside a 200 ft diameter hemi-spherical radome
- the Post Office station at Goonhilly on the Lizard peninsula, Cornwall, with an 85 ft diameter, 870 ton steerable open parabolic dish aerial
- a French PTT/CNET station at Pleumer Bodou, Brittany, with an aerial identical with the ATT/Bell aerial at Andover

Building the Post Office Earth Station

Following the agreement with NASA in February 1961, the planning and organisation of the provision of the PO Earth Station became the prime responsibility of the PO ED Space Communication Systems Branch, of which I was then Head. It was a formidable task, with a site yet to be determined, the type of aerial undecided and the highly specialised microwave receiving and transmitting equipment yet to be designed. And the deadline was the launch of Telstar – scheduled for July 1962 – giving us barely a year and a half to be ready for the first ever transmission of television signals across the Atlantic on which the eyes of the world would be focused.

The uniqueness of the project and the significance of a successful outcome for the future of world communications meant that co-operation – with a total absence of bureaucratic formality – was immediately forthcoming from other Government Departments, the UK Telecommunications Industry, and above all within the PO Engineering Department itself. The contributions of the Radio Experimental Branch at Dollis Hill, headed by F.J.D. Taylor, to the design and provision of the specialised transmitting and receiving equipment, were vital to the success of the project, and W.E. Thomson at the Research Branch, Dollis Hill, gave valuable guidance on the computer facilities needed for satellite tracking.[14][15]

79

There were also fortuitous events that helped towards the final successful outcome:

- my sabbatical year with the Bell Laboratories in 1956 enabled me to meet Dr Gene O'Neill, who became Head of Project Telstar and a good friend
- John Taylor and I were next-door neighbours at our homes in Wembley Park, which led to close co-operation between HQ and Dollis Hill, often cemented by a glass of Scotch on Sunday morning!
- my daughter Frances, then at North London Collegiate School, had a school friend whose father in the Ministry of Defence introduced John Taylor and me to Tom Husband, who had designed the giant 240 ft diameter radio-astronomy telescope at Jodrell Bank (it was Tom Husband and his civil engineering firm who designed and built the massive 870 ton steerable aerial at Goonhilly).

The Government Services Electronic Research Laboratory at Baldock was especially helpful in designing and manufacturing the high-power 5 kW travelling-wave tube needed for the Earth station transmitter output stage. And the Mullard Research Laboratories, Salfords, contributed the low-noise, liquid-helium-cooled 'Maser' receiver pre-amplifier – a vital component in view of the very low-level signals received from Telstar.

A site on the Lizard Peninsula, Cornwall, for the PO Earth station had been chosen with the intention that it would shorten the over-sea path to the USA (and thus extend the period of mutual visibility for satellites such as Telstar), be suitable for satellites in an Equatorial Earth orbit and minimise the possibility of interference from terrestrial micro-wave radio-relay systems that shared with space communication the 4 GHz and 6 GHz frequency bands. It was interesting that the satellite Earth station site on the Lizard was close to that at Poldhu used by Marconi for the first transatlantic Morse telegraph transmissions in 1901. (See plate 17)

And so, by July 1962 all was in readiness at Goonhilly for

the launch of Telstar, albeit with some trepidation, since up till that time none of the complex receiving equipment and the computer-controlled satellite tracking system had actually been tested with a moving satellite.

The First Television Transmissions Across the Atlantic and the Telstar Tests

The Telstar satellite was launched from Cape Canaveral at 0835 GMT on 10 July 1962, but on the first pass across the Atlantic only weak signals were received at Goonhilly. This was soon realised as arising from a misunderstanding with Bell Laboratories as to whether the signals transmitted by the satellite were right- or left-hand polarised, i.e. whether the electric vector in the radiated wave was spinning clockwise or counter-clockwise. The wave polariser in the Goonhilly aerial was then readjusted, and on the next pass of Telstar, two and a half hours later, excellent television pictures were received from Andover. (See plates 12 and 13) To the French at Pleumer Bodou must go the honour of receiving the first pictures, but on the next pass Goonhilly transmitted the first ever live television programme to the USA – an impromptu tour of Goonhilly with an introduction by Capt C.F. Booth, Deputy Engineer-in-Chief of the Post Office.

These proceedings were broadcast live on television throughout the world, with commentaries by Raymond Baxter for the BBC and Ian Trethowan for Independent Television. We, the actors, had the feeling of 'walking a tightrope' with millions of people waiting for us to fall off if we failed! However, I remember being very impressed with Raymond Baxter's ability to turn my technical explanations into easy-to-understand language for the television viewers.

Looking back, it is not difficult to recall the elated atmosphere at Goonhilly after success had been achieved in this epoch-making event. As engineers we had lived through a year of strenuous endeavour, had overcome many technical and logistic problems – and had survived the final 'tightrope walk'. To celebrate, the ITV had provided a crate of the best French champagne – and it is no wonder that night Goonhilly looked remarkably like an air-borne satellite Earth station!

There followed televised exchanges between Sir Ronald German, Director General of the Post Office, and Mr McNeely, President of the American Telephone and Telegraph Co, who spoke of 'the thrill of communicating through a dot in space'. And Queen Elizabeth herself referred to Telstar as 'the invisible focus of a million eyes'.

The extensive programme of technical tests that followed clearly established that active communication satellites could provide high-quality, stable channels for the transmission of telephony (600 or more fdm channels), facsimile, data and television signals. A Post Office ED initiative, supported by the BBC Research Department, established that satellite channels could transmit colour television signals satisfactorily – a stringent test of any transmission system. To convince our Bell Laboratories colleagues, these transmissions were made on US NTSC 525-lines colour standards.[16]

It was a source of some pride to the Post Office that its 'do it yourself' approach to satellite Earth station design, with its heavy open parabolic-dish reflector aerial, as compared with the Bell Laboratories' large radome-covered horn aerial, had achieved an even better performance at a fraction of the cost. The performance advantage lay in the fact that in the PO design there was no radome to reflect from raindrops on its surface radio noise from the relatively hot earth – an effect which caused occasional 'outages' in reception of the weak signals from the satellite. The basic open parabolic reflector design later became general practice in the ongoing development of satellite communication systems.

There followed in 1963 project Syncom – the achievement of the equatorial 'stationary' orbit at 22,300 miles height, by engineers of the Hughes Aircraft Co in the USA. And with this A.C. Clarke's vision of 1945 had become reality and the stage was set for worldwide communication by satellite.

10

Technological Advances of the Postwar Years

It seems appropriate at this stage in my autobiography to put aside matters in which I had some direct personal involvement and to review briefly the remarkable advances that have been made in telecommunications and broadcasting during the past half century. The following account is based on the opening chapter of my book *The Communications Miracle*.

The present-day world telecommunication network is the most complex, extensive and costly of mankind's technological creations and, it could be claimed, the most useful. Together with sound and television broadcasting, telecommunication provides the nervous system essential for the social, economic and political development of civilization. It enables any user of one of the 1,000 million or more of the world total of telephones in homes and offices, cars, ships and aircraft to communicate with any other, regardless of distance. It provides fast distribution of documents by facsimile transmission and nearly instantaneous electronic delivery of letter mail – 'e-mail'.

The transmission of television signals is not only worldwide – it now provides pictures from far distant planets of the Solar System. The use of television for business conferences between distant offices speeds up decision-making and minimises the need for travel.

And a whole new art of information access, exchange and processing information – information technology (IT) – has developed whereby users in home and office can gain access via the telecommunication network to virtually unlimited pages of information, visually displayed, from local or remote data banks, and interact with the information thus obtained.

The future impact of information technology could well be immense. By removing the need to travel to communicate, the vast waste of human and material resources required to provide ever-expanding road and rail facilities for countless millions of commuters day-by-day from homes to city offices could well be minimised. And by diverting much office work from large cities to villages and small towns, the quality of life could be enhanced for many and the rural economy benefited.

This massive development in the scale and range of telecommunication-based services has become possible by a remarkable and continuous evolution in system concepts and the supporting technology, much of which has taken place in the last few decades, but of which the mathematical, scientific and conceptual origins can be traced back a century or more.

As to the advances that telecommunication technology has made, one has only to compare the primitive slow-speed telegraphs, the pole-mounted copper wires providing a few telephone circuits between cities and the manual telephone exchanges of the early 1900s, with today's coaxial cable, microwave radio-relay, optical fibre cables and satellites providing almost unlimited communication capacity on a worldwide scale. And the process of making connections between users has been made almost instantaneous by fast, computer-controlled electronic exchanges.

Intercontinental telephone communication, e.g. across the Atlantic, was limited until the 1950s to a dozen or so circuits carried on short-wave radio, and live transatlantic television was not possible. Today communication satellites and optical fibre submarine cables provide telephone circuits numbered in hundreds of thousands, and many high-quality television channels.

Device technology has made massive leaps forward, from the thermionic valves of the early 1900s to the revolutionary invention of the solid-state transistor and micro-technology that puts millions of transistors on a few square millimetres of silicon – the 'micro-chip'. These devices have made it possible to carry out, reliably and economically, circuit functions and signal-processing of great complexity. They have facilitated the

1. Parents: Emily Eliza (Née Clothier) and William James Bray (1887-1965)

2. Grandparent:
William James Bray (1854-1932)

3. Grandparent:
Caroline Clothier (Née Sanders)

4. Portsmouth Naval Dockyard: Home of Nelson's flagship *HMS Victory* and the Dockyard School where I received technical education during my apprenticeship (1928-1933)

5. City and Guilds Engineering College, South Kensington. A part of Imperial College, London where I studied for an M.Sc (Eng) degree (1933-1935)

6. The Post Office Research Station Dollis Hill, North-West London. The portico of the main building, opened in 1933, bore the inscription: 'Research is the Door to Tomorrow' and 'To Strive, To Seek, To Find' Tennyson. Use of the site by the P.O. ceased in 1976, after more than 50 years

7. The Post Office Research Centre at Martlesham, Suffolk (now British Telecom Laboratories). Opened by H.M. The Queen on 21 November 1975. From left to right: administration block with offices, library and restaurant; radio tower and lifts; main laboratory block; water tower and lifts; workshop and research services block

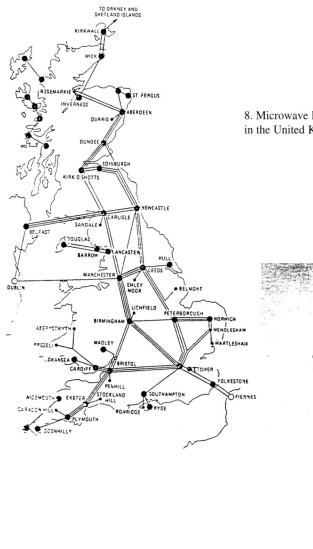

8. Microwave Radio-Relay Trunk Network in the United Kingdom

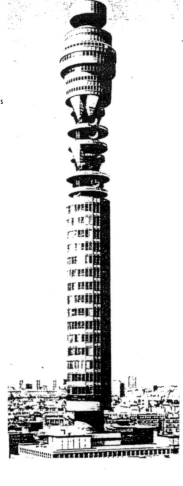

9. British Telecom Tower (London)
Focal point of the Network

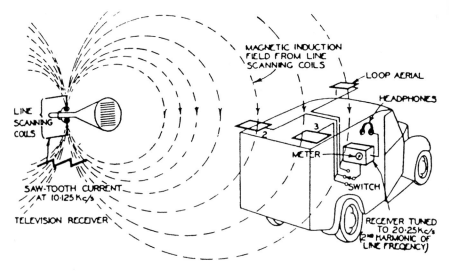

10. Principles

11. Post Office Television Detection Van (1952)

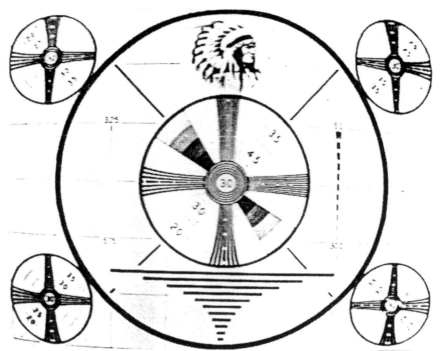

12. 'Indian Head' Test Card received at Goonhilly from ATT/BTL Satellite Ground Station, Andover, Maine from Telstar on 11 July 1962

13. Map of U.K. transmitted from Goonhilly via Telstar on 11 July 1962

The first tests via the Telstar Satellite in July 1962. These 'Test Cards' one from Goonhilly, U.K. and the other from Andover, U.S.A. marked the first ever contacts by live television across the Atlantic.

14. *Sjøhest* moored in the Deben river July 1983

15. Grandad and
Granddaughter Laura

16. Margaret Bray
1911-1998

17. Post Office satellite communication ground station aerial No. 1 at Goonhilly, Cornwall (1962)
The original oil painting was painted by Ken Howard, ARA, shortly after the first transmission of TV across the Atlantic by Telstar. It was used for a Post Office stamp to commemorate the event, and the painting itself is now in my study, having been presented at my retirement dinner (after falling off the P.O. boardroom wall!)

introduction of new system concepts, such as pulse-code modulation and digital techniques, that have improved the quality of signals transmitted over long distances, provided more channels in the radio-frequency spectrum and facilitated the storage of video signals.

The new devices and system concepts have transformed telecommunications, sound and television broadcasting, and computing to a degree beyond imagination half a century ago. They have created massive new electronic industries and given birth to information technology with its ever-growing impact on the way people live and work.

The technology of sound broadcasting has evolved from the monaural amplitude-modulation, long- and medium-wave services of the 1920s to the high-quality stereophonic frequency-modulation VHF services of the mid-1900s and the digital-modulation services now coming into service. The introduction of colour into television broadcasting in the latter half of the twentieth century was in itself a scientific, technological and manufacturing achievement of the first order.

It was against this technological background that I returned from the PO ED HQ in London to the PO Research Branch at Dollis Hill in 1963 – a move which gave me the opportunity to see what my research colleagues had been doing whilst I 'had been pottering about with microwaves and satellites', as a kind friend put it!

11

The Research Branch at Dollis Hill 1963–66

I must admit that in returning to Dollis Hill in 1963 from the City, it was with a slight feeling of despondency. After savouring the broader atmosphere of Engineering Department HQ, the excitements of Telstar, activities on the international front with the CCIR, and a Commonwealth Fund Fellowship in the USA, to return to the same office at Dollis Hill that I had left several years earlier did seem something of an anticlimax!

However, in 1965 I was appointed Deputy Director of Research at Dollis Hill, then headed as Director by Dr G. Metson, MC, whom I had first met in Northern Ireland during my probationary training period. This appointment was essentially concerned with the 'systems' side of research and opened up a new and interesting field of future activities. From being very much a 'radio' engineer I had now to understand and support the development of:

- submarine telephone cable systems with repeaters based on long-life transistors
- advanced exchange switching systems controlled by computers
- pulse-code modulation digital techniques for transmission and switching

All this had to be done within the context of the aims of PO Research, defined in the 1960s as:

'The study of new materials, devices and system concepts of potential value to the telecommunication and postal businesses and, where appropriate, the demonstration of technical feasibility by the advance development of prototype equipment and field trials.'

Whilst research often enabled limitations of existing technologies to be remedied, more significantly it created new technologies that enabled existing services to be provided at lower cost and new services to be created. This work was often carried out in co-operation with UK industry to expedite the transition from research through development to production of equipment and use in the field. The results of research enabled the PO Engineering Department at HQ to prepare technical and performance specifications for the equipment it needed to meet service demands.

The 75th Anniversary (1906–81) volume of the *Post Office Electrical Engineers Journal* gives a comprehensive survey of the telecommunications and postal engineering activities carried out by the PO Engineering Department in that period. It contains a paper on 'Research' by my colleague Dr J.R. Tillman, Deputy Director of Research, that gives a detailed picture of the wide scope and depth of research at Dollis Hill in the 25 years to 1981.[17] In this field the PO ED Research Branch achieved a worldwide reputation – second only (and not always second!) to the prestigious Bell Telephone Laboratories in the USA.

Certain 'highlights' in research achievement, and the innovative engineering projects they led to, are especially worthy of note – they include the following:

- the development and manufacture of long-life thermionic valves for submarine cable repeaters, used in the first transatlantic submarine telephone cable in 1956 and several later cables
- the development and manufacture of high-performance, high-reliability silicon-based transistors for submarine cable systems, used on UK–Portugal and Canada–Bermuda cables in 1968 (the replacement of valves by transistors in repeater design provided many more telephone circuits)

87

- the work on microwave radio-relay systems that introduced travelling-wave tube amplifiers (a world first in 1952), and the international standardisation of microwave radio-relay systems in 1959
- the creation of new system concepts and the appropriate device technology that enabled the replacement of earlier analogue amplitude modulation transmission systems by pulse-code modulation digital techniques for transmission and exchange switching; (the PO-designed digital exchange at Empress, London, opened in 1968, was a world first); these developments provided a foundation for the Integrated Service Digital Network (ISDN) that brought together telephone, facsimile, data and video services in a common framework, with substantial economic and operational advantages
- the development of low-loss optical fibres, solid-state lasers and light amplifiers that made possible a vast expansion of the communications capacity that could be provided economically on local area, inter-city and inter-continental links (the first example of the latter was the transatlantic optical fibre cable, opened in 1988, that provided some 40,000 telephone circuits and several television channels)
- the pioneering work on satellite communication system technology that led to the first transmissions of television across the Atlantic in 1962 via the PO Earth station at Goonhilly and the establishment of an economic and effective basis for Earth station design
- the PO 'Viewdata' (later 'Prestel') system, enabling a telephone user to obtain access to unlimited data and information that could be displayed on his television receiver screen; first demonstrated by the PO Research Branch in 1971, Viewdata brought it home to the PO Administration that it had an important role to play in visual as well as telephone communications; Viewdata was an important pre-cursor to the Internet and the World-Wide Web.

There were many other important areas of PO research – for example, the 'lightweight' submarine cable invented by Dr R.A. Brockbank which, by placing the mechanical strength of the cable inside an inner steel core instead of the outside armouring, greatly reduced the size and weight that the cable ships had to carry and thus the cost of submarine telephone cables.

Special equipment was devised for use on the PO cable ships to facilitate the handling of many miles of submarine cables with repeaters at intervals of a few kilometres, and equipment to locate and recover faulty repeaters at depths of a mile or more in the deep oceans.

Postal engineering research was busy devising faster and more accurate machines for sorting the parcel and letter mail. Letter mail sorting machines had been devised using a manually operated keyboard to place phosphor dots on letters, which could then be read electronically and sorted by destination. Research led by Dr A.W. Coombs enabled typewritten addresses to be read directly without human intervention, faster and with a high standard of accuracy; however, handwritten addresses proved to be a tough nut to crack.

And thus in the 1960s and 1970s my professional life was passed in a stimulating and challenging research environment with like-minded and supportive colleagues, who shared the feeling that the work we were engaged on was in the public good and abundantly worthwhile.

12

Director of Research and New Laboratories at Martlesham, Suffolk 1966–75

With my appointment as Director of Research of the Post Office in 1966 and until my retirement in 1975 the joys of hands-on participation in the development of new technology largely disappeared and other, more challenging, responsibilities emerged. It was a time when transistor and microchip technology was advancing rapidly, optical fibres were looking more promising, exchange switching was emerging into a computer-controlled electronic form and above all, the digital revolution was beginning to take shape.[1]

Fortunately I was supported by three Deputy Directors, each an expert in his own field, who patiently kept their Director 'on the rails'! In particular I have to thank Dr J.R. Tillman for enlightening me on the physics of the micro-technology and optical fibres, H.B. Law for unravelling the mysteries of digital switching and E.W. Ayers for guidance on visual systems such as Viewdata/Prestel.

I discovered on a visit to Bell Laboratories that Julius Molnar, the Deputy President of Bell, had like me, been primarily a transmission engineer and had to 'learn switching' late in his career – an operation he described as akin to 'papering over the cracks'!

As Director I had to oversee the planning and building of new Research Laboratories at Martlesham, Suffolk, and the movement of some 1,500 staff from Dollis Hill to the new location. (See plate 7)

New Laboratories at Martlesham

The Post Office Radio Experimental and Research Branches had been located at Dollis Hill for more than 50 years, from a beginning in wooden huts on a farm site to a Lutyens-designed building that housed the Research Branch from 1933.

The need to move away from Dollis Hill arose because the site was too small to allow for growth in staff and research facilities. More space was needed for field work and several of the buildings erected hurriedly during the war years needed replacement. Furthermore, a majority of the staff travelled long distances across London and spent many hours getting to and from work – a wastage of time and energy.

A new site on a disused RAF airfield was eventually chosen in East Anglia that met the need for ample space and was conveniently placed for access by rail and road to the PO ED HQ in London. Agreement on the location was the subject of detailed and sometimes protracted negotiations with staff associations to ensure that reasonable aspirations as to the availability of housing, schools and shopping facilities could be met.

The design of the new laboratories had to follow – at least in outline – standard PO and Ministry of Public Buildings and Works procedures, which required a detailed 'Schedule of Requirements' for guidance of the architect. This, because of the specialised nature of the laboratories and the work in them, involved the scientists and engineers of the Research Branch in lengthy discussions with the Ministry and its architect to determine their present and anticipated future requirements. And since the buildings were to be provided under the authority of the PO HQ Buildings and Welfare Department there were also strict standards, already agreed with staff Unions, on office and laboratory accommodation and safety aspects, that had to be observed. My colleagues C.F. Floyd and A. Webster were heavily involved in this work.[18]

Key features in the design that was eventually agreed were the following:

- air-conditioning throughout to ensure a controlled atmosphere
- freedom from noise and mechanical vibration
- maximum flexibility in the usage of space
- maximum usage of 'natural daylight' in offices and regularly occupied laboratories.

The avoidance of noise and mechanical vibration required careful attention to soundproofing and insulation of lifts from the main building. Flexibility in the utilisation of space was achieved by modular construction of the laboratories and offices with moveable partitions, and modular distribution of services such as telephones, electrical power, water etc. The staff side claim to maximum use of 'natural daylight' required much ingenuity to avoid wastage of space in the inner core areas of the laboratory block.

The design that eventually evolved provided:

- an 'administration' block with management offices, library, lecture theatre, library, conference rooms and staff restaurant
- a six-storey laboratory block, with external lifts, a 'water' tower which included offices and a 'radio' tower, the latter accommodating a radio laboratory and microwave radio-relay telephone and video (television conference) links to the trunk network and PO ED HQ in London
- a single-storey workshop and research services block

The construction work on site did not progress smoothly, however; the main contractor failed, partly because he was heavily committed to another large project in Africa and partly through a strike of workmen that then seemed endemic in the building industry. Another contractor had to be found and sub-contracts re-negotiated. The delay of some years before the new buildings were usable meant that a carefully planned move of some 1,500 staff had to be reorganised, and use made for a time of temporary 'single storey' cabins for offices and laboratories. In spite of these hazards the new laboratories were completed, substantially on budget cost, and opened in 1975.

The movement from London to East Anglia of the large number of staff involved required careful preparation and consultation with staff organisations on matters such as housing, schools and compensation for the cost of moving. This work, which devolved mainly on C.F. Floyd and A. Webster, was carried out very effectively and nearly all the key staff from Dollis Hill came to Martlesham. Others, mainly those at Dollis Hill, approaching retirement age, were found work elsewhere in the London PO region. The move was greatly facilitated by the PO purchase of a Ministry of Defence housing estate near Felixstowe, for use as 'staging-post' housing that could be rented by staff for up to six months whilst seeking permanent accommodation.

The new Laboratories were formally opened by Her Majesty the Queen on 21 November 1975, shortly after my retirement from the PO, when a new Director, C.A. May, had taken over. I recall that, at the celebration lunch, HM asked me '...and how were the families who moved from London settling down in Suffolk?' It was with pleasure that I was able to reply that 'they were much enjoying the new environment and the better quality of life that this pleasant area of England offered'. And of course for many of the husbands it meant far less time travelling to and from work, and more time with their families.

On the occasion of my retirement in July 1975, my good friend Charles May told me that it had been decided to call the rather splendid lecture theatre at Martlesham 'the John Bray Lecture Theatre' – a decision much appreciated by my family as well as myself. The adjective 'splendid' is perhaps justified – the lecture theatre seats 450 people, has a large stage, excellent audio-visual and simultaneous translation facilities. It is only fair to recall that I was once accused by a PO Board member of having planned the lecture theatre for 'a simultaneous performance of *Oklahoma, South Pacific* and *Annie Get Your Gun*!

It was later a source of considerable satisfaction to those who had helped to create the modern, well-equipped and staffed Research Laboratories at Martlesham that they had also provided for British Telecom a major asset which would contribute to its success in the future.

Chair of Telecommunication System Studies at Essex University

Although telecommunications in the UK during the 1950s was becoming a major growth industry, with an investment in the national network exceeding £1,000 million and a substantial export trade, there was little in the way of advanced studies at university level. For example, exchange switching and traffic theory was hardly taught at all; this was dominated by the long-established and virtually static electro-mechanical Strowger switching system, the lore of which was mainly confined to the Post Office and the exchange equipment manufacturing industry. But with the advent of computer-controlled electronic switching systems requiring complex software support, digital transmission techniques and solid-state device micro-technology, the scene was changing and there was a clear and expanding need for graduate recruits to the PO and the telecommunication industry with an appropriate technology background.

Realising this need, and with the support of my Deputy Directors, Dr J.R. Tillman and H.B. Law, we persuaded in 1965 the Postmaster General, John Stonehouse, to fund, initially for five years but later extended to the present time, a Chair of Telecommunication System Studies at Essex University. The Chair was to cover all aspects of telecommunication, from system concepts and technology to economic and human factors, and to carry out research where appropriate. Essex was chosen for its proximity to the PO Laboratories at Martlesham, as we envisaged there might be interchange, e.g. in teaching and research projects.

The first occupant of the Chair, and for many following years, was Professor K. Cattermole, who had worked at the Standard Telecommunication Laboratories, Harlow, and published an authoritative textbook on PCM digital techniques. Under his guidance the Chair became a valuable training ground for PO, UK industry and overseas students, and carried out much original research in telecommunications. It became my pleasure to visit Essex University from time to time, in company with Kenneth Cadbury, then Assistant Managing Director of the PO, to see progress in the work of the Chair and arrange further funding.

This academic initiative in telecommunication studies was quickly followed by other UK universities, notably at Imperial College (Kensington), University College (London) and Aston (Birmingham), and at a number of polytechnics and colleges of advanced education.

My small part in the creation of the Chair received unexpected acknowledgement in 1976 when I received, at the hand of Lord Butler, then Chancellor of the Exchequer, an Honorary Doctorate of Essex University. I recall walking down the stairs of the University, wearing one of those odd medieval hats, arm-in-arm with the charming and much-respected Lady Wooton (later Baroness Wooton), who also received an Honorary Doctorate from Essex. Lady Wooton had been the first woman in the UK to be awarded a university degree, from Cambridge, many years earlier.

Overseas Lecture Tours – (1) South Africa 1972

This visit arose from an invitation by the South African Institute of Electrical Engineers to give their Bernard Price Memorial Lecture, initially at the University of Witwatersrand, Johannesburg, and afterwards at universities in Durban and Cape Town.

My wife and I were accompanied throughout this visit by Mr Allan Bennett, then President of the SA IEE and Chief Engineer of the SA Post Office, and his wife – an arrangement that added much to the pleasure of the visit. We were able, when I was not giving lectures or consultancy work for the SA Post Office, to visit the Kruger National Park, the countryside around Durban and Table Mountain, Cape Town.

We also enjoyed some pleasant sailing off Cape Town to Robin Island, thanks to a friendly yachtsman from the Royal Cape Yacht Club. Little did we know, as we watched the dolphins playing amongst the waves off Robin Island, that this was where Nelson Mandela – later to become President of the Republic of South Africa – was imprisoned!

The theme of the lecture was 'Evolutionary Telecommunications and Ecological Man' – the advances in system concepts and technology that were making possible a major expansion in the scale of telecommunication services and the introduction of new services, and the impact that these could have on man's ecology, that is his ability to control and improve his environment, for example by minimising the need to travel to communicate. Given in 1972, well before the era of computer-based information technology and the Internet had come into being, the lecture nevertheless gave a reasonably accurate prediction of the shape of things to come.

Overseas Lecture Tours – (2) Australia 1973

This visit came from an invitation from the Australian Post Office to give the opening lecture at a two-day symposium to celebrate the Golden Jubilee of the APO Research Laboratories in Melbourne. The theme I chose was 'The Integration of Telecommunications' – the ability of new technology to bring together telegraph, telephone, data, facsimile and video services in a common system (foreshadowing the 'Integrated Services Digital Network' concept), and the economic and operational advantages that this could offer. I also delivered a companion lecture on 'The Expanding Role of Telecommunications' as a keynote address to the Australian National Radio and Electronic Convention in Sydney.

Friendly relations had long existed between the British and Australian Post Office Departments; these included the interchange of research staff and APO engineering assistance in building the PO satellite Earth station at Goonhilly in 1962.

During this visit I was engaged by the APO in a consultancy role which involved discussions with R.W. Turnbull, Director General Development and Research, and P.R. Brett, Assistant DG Research.

The visit was not without its lighter side. I had spoken in my lecture on the possibilities of electronic mail using the telephone network overnight when traffic was light (this was well before the advent of e-mail). In a Press interview that followed the lecture a charming young lady from the Press asked 'Could she send love letters by electronic mail?' My answer: 'Yes, of course.' 'And how much would it cost?' My light-hearted reply (she was very charming): 'For you darling – nothing!'

The first hint of trouble came the next morning when my wife, listening to her bedside radio, heard the whole of this rather indiscreet conversation over the air and, not unnaturally, wanted to know what it was all about! It then became clear that my charming lady interviewer had a concealed tape recorder of which she made good, if unauthorised, use.

But worse was to come. At my next APO consultation meeting with the Assistant Director General he began by saying 'As I was listening on my car radio this morning, what did I hear but you offering free transmission of love letters over the APO telephone system!' However, all was soon forgiven and APO/BPO relations soon resumed their normal friendly course.

A final grace note to my APO visit was sailing a racing yacht in Sydney Harbour thanks to the hospitality of the Royal Australian Yacht Club and the kindness of the Managing Director of Plessey, Australia.

A Retirement Dinner

With my retirement from the PO in July 1975 came an enjoyable retirement dinner with colleagues and wives, at which I was presented with much ceremony a volume labelled 'This Is Your Life' (sadly, this turned out to be a catalogue of the many radio and research reports I had written over the years!). Much more agreeable was a large oil painting of the first satellite Earth Station Aerial built at Goonhilly, Cornwall, in 1962. According to my good friend Jim Merriman, PO Board Member, who presented me with the painting, it had fallen off the Boardroom wall! Be that as it may, it now hangs on my study wall and provides an ever-present reminder of the exciting events that followed the launch of Telstar. Mine has been an immensely rewarding professional career, one in which I have been privileged to play a small part in building today's world telecommunication systems and information technology that may yet help to create a more prosperous and peaceful world. From a schoolboy building a crystal radio set to an engineer helping to span the Atlantic with live television – what a marvellous journey it has been!

13

Professional Institutions

Belonging to a professional institution that functions as a 'learned society', enabling him to keep up to date with technical developments in his profession and, in due time, to contribute to the fund of technical knowledge, is an essential for an engineer wishing to advance in his profession. The professional institution has in turn a responsibility for keeping Government aware of developments in engineering that may have an impact on the nation's economy and well-being, and for supporting training and educational facilities appropriate to the profession. In my case the professional institution was the Institution of Electrical Engineers, with its elegant headquarters building at Savoy Place, by the Thames near Waterloo Bridge, London.

The Institution of Electrical Engineers

The IEE is the largest professional engineering organisation in Europe and one with the longest history, going back to the early 1900s, when the famous mathematician Oliver Heaviside was a member and it was called the Society of Telegraph Engineers.

I joined a Junior Section of the IEE when I was a student at City and Guilds Engineering College in Kensington (1932–35), and throughout my professional career had an active involvement with the Institution. This began as a member of the early Radio Section of the IEE which became the Electronics Division when electronics assumed an increasingly important role in manufacturing industry, telecommunications and broadcasting.

Over the years 1947 to 1965 I contributed a number of technical papers to the IEE Proceedings and Conference publications, covering such topics as:

- the testing of communication-type radio receivers (1947)
- the design of single-sideband radio equipment
- a fading machine for the study of a frequency-selective fading
- microwave propagation testing equipment
- the travelling-wave tube as a microwave frequency shifter
- radio wave propagation above 30 MHz*
- VHF propagation by ionospheric scattering and its application to long-distance communication*
- the standardisation of international microwave radio-relay systems
- the potential of communication satellites
- the worldwide relaying of television by artificial earth satellites
- technical aspects of the design of communication satellite systems (1965)

Looking back, the themes of these papers showed an interesting broadening in my range of technical interest. Other IEE activities involved Chairmanship at various times of Professional Groups on Radio Systems, Microwave Techniques, Wave Propagation and Aerials.

An interesting task, involving much study at weekends of membership application forms, was the IEE Membership Committee. The IEE has strict standards as to the educational qualification and professional experience required of its members, who were tested by interview. The latter required

---

* with Dr J.A. Saxton and staff of Radio Research Station, Slough

each applicant for membership to provide an organisational tree showing his position in the organisation for which he worked – from which the interviewer often learned a good deal about the organisation of the UK electrical industry!

In due time I became a chartered electrical engineer and Fellow of the IEE (FIEE), and received along the way Ambrose Fleming, Radio Section and Electronics Division Premium Awards for my technical papers. I am especially proud to have received in 1977 the IEE J.J. Thomson Medal for (it says on the medal!) 'Distinguished contribution to electronic engineering'.

But my mind goes back to a very young engineer about to make his first contribution to a discussion following the presentation of a paper by a more senior member at the IEE. To his horror, all those who preceded him in the discussion made every point he had in mind and did so more effectively than he could have hoped for. Out of sheer nervousness he rapidly departed from the Lecture Theatre before his name was called! But this chastening experience did create a determination to overcome such nervousness and learn the something of the art of public speaking – which in much later years served him well when, for example, he had to present, as International Chairman of CCIR Study Group IX, a major document on the standardisation of radio-relay systems for approval at a Plenary Session of the International Telecommunication Union in Geneva.

The City and Guilds of London Institute

As I mentioned in Chapter 3 of Part 1, my studies at City and Guilds Engineering College gained me qualifications of Associate Membership (ACGI) and the Diploma of Imperial College (DIC).

In 1967 I was awarded a Fellowship of the City and Guilds of London Institute (FCGI) – a privilege which includes an annual luncheon with many of the Fellows, usually held in the delightful home of the Rector of Imperial College, in South Kensington. It is an occasion to meet old colleagues and friends from the academic and industrial worlds, and to hear at first hand reports from the City and Guilds Institute on national progress in craft training, and from the Rector of progress and problems at Imperial College.'

The Royal Academy of Engineering

To be elected, as I was in 1978, a Fellow of the Royal Academy of Engineering (FEng) a very considerable honour, since the Academy comprises some 1,000 of the most distinguished engineers in the UK. The Academy is not only a learned society in its own right, in which engineering matters of major importance are discussed and debated, it has become an important channel of communication between the whole engineering profession and Government. It is thus in a position not only to help to maintain the status of engineers, but also to ensure that the contribution that engineering can make to the national economy and well-being is known and acted upon.

In a more personal matter, it was a past President of the Academy, Sir William Barlow, FEng, who gave me valuable support and encouragement in writing and publishing my book *The Communications Miracle* by writing: 'A wonderful and accurate description of how it all happened by one of the engineers who made it happen – an inspiration to prospective young engineers.'

A World-Wide Web Site

In 1997 I had a telephone call from a John May, whom I had quoted, (p. 343 of *The Communications Miracle*) for a definition of the Internet, saying 'Would I like to join him as a Technical Consultant to himself as Editor of a new World-Wide Web Site on "A Modern History of Communications, Computing and the Media"'. This I was delighted to do – the site is now in being and is to be found at:
http://www.acclarke.co.uk

The site has been funded by Cable and Wireless in acknowledgement of the massive contributions made by Arthur C. Clarke with the invention of satellite communication and his writings on science fiction.

In it, by clicking on the 'Credits' icon and the word 'bray', you can find a personal essay about *The Communications Miracle*!

References

(1) *The Communications Miracle – The Telecommunication Pioneers from Morse to the Information Superhighway* by John Bray, pub. Plenum of New York and London, 1995

(2) *Monopoly and Competition in British Telecommunications – The Past, Present and the Future* by John Harper; pub. Pinter, 1997

(3) *Memoirs of a Telecommunications Engineer* by John Bray; pub. privately 1982. Limited number of copies available via e-mail (bray@btinternet.com)

(4) *The Secret War* by B. Johnson, pub. BBC, 1978; describes Prof. R.V. Jones's role in World War II

(5) *The Beam Benders, RAF 90 (Signals Wing) 1940–1945* by Laurie Brettingham; pub. Midland, 1997

(6) *Codebreakers, The Inside Story of Bletchley Park*, edited by F.H. Hinsley and Alan Strip, pub. Oxford University Press, 1993

(7) *Three Steps to Victory* by Sir Robert Watson-Watt; pub. Odhams Press, 1957

(8) 'The Standardization of International Microwave Radio-Relay Systems' by W.J. Bray, *Proceedings of the Institution of Electrical Engineers*, Vol. 108B, 1961

(9) *Post Office Contributions to the Early History of the Development of Television in the UK* by W.J. Bray; IEE Conference publication on the history of television, Nov. 1986

(10) 'Extra-terrestrial Relays: Can Rocket Stations Give World-wide Coverage?' by A.C. Clarke, *Wireless World*, October 1945

(11) 'Orbital Radio Relays', by J.R. Pierce, *Jet Propulsion*, April 1955

(12) *The Beginnings of Satellite Communication* by J.R. Pierce, San Francisco Press, 1968

(13) 'A Study of Satellite Systems for Civil Communication', *Royal Aircraft Establishment Report No GW26*, March 1961. Published in shortened form in book *Telecommunication Satellites*, edited by R.W. Gatland, Iliffe Books Ltd, 1964

(14) 'Satellite Communication Systems' by W.J. Bray, *PO Elect. Eng. Journal, 55*, July 1962

(15) 'Equipment and Testing Facilities at the Experimental Satellite Ground Station, Goonhilly Downs, Cornwall', by F.J.D. Taylor, *PO Elec. Eng. Journal, 55*, July 1962

(16) 'Preliminary Results of the Project Telstar Communication Satellite Tests and Demonstrations' by W.J. Bray and F.J.D. Taylor, *PO Elec. Eng. Journal, 55*, October 1962

(17) 'Inst. PO Engineers 75th Anniversary 1906 – 81' *Post Office Electrical Engineers Journal, Vol. 74, Part 3*, October 1981. 'Research by Dr J.R. Tillman, pp 282–97

(18) 'The Design of Martlesham Research Centre' and 'The Move to Martlesham' by C.F. Floyd, *PO Elec. Eng. Journal*, Oct. 1996, Jan. 1997 and April 1997

PART 3

A PERSONAL LIFE

Even a dedicated professional engineer has a personal life – known perhaps in full only to family and close friends. The first part of this autobiography – 'A Learning Life' – has given some account of the life of the child, schoolboy, college student and apprentice during the first two decades of their existence; it remains to say something about the life of the octogenarian who survived after six more decades, and to establish the fact that it was not wholly taken up by the marvels of technology.

There are difficulties of course in writing about one's own personal life, but there are advantages too in that age confers the right to look at one's own past follies with a more understanding, and perhaps forgiving, eye.

What emerges is a picture seen from the inside and thus inevitably has a bias, the extent of which only those near to the writer can and will judge, I hope in a kindly way!

PART 3
A PERSONAL LIFE

1

Reading, Writing and Poetry

Reading

The habit of reading, inherited I am sure from my mother as recounted in Part 1, is one that I pursued from my earliest days. It has from the beginning been on an omnivorous and exploratory scale – guided only by what stimulated my imagination and interest.

As a schoolboy my reading could hardly be classed as 'educational' in the strict sense – it seems to have consisted mainly of paperbacked and rather tattered books about the adventures of Sexton Blake and Tinker, passed on to me by a kindly uncle, and weekly journals about Greyfriars public school and a plump character called Bunter. Some of this reading was carried out against parental disapproval in bed after 'lights out' with the aid of a home-made battery-operated electric torch.

Rather more upmarket was the monthly *Boys Own Paper* which contained, in addition to adventure stories, articles on how to make toys and items of interest to boys. One of these I remember well was a wooden-framed canvas-covered canoe, constructed with the help of my sail-maker grandfather and sailed off Southsea Beach. However, the design must have been somewhat faulty because the canoe proved to be remarkably unstable and liable to tip the occupant into the sea at the least provocation! It was some years later, when I had become a Dockyard apprentice, that I learned from the ship design course of the need to keep the hull 'centre of gravity' below the 'centre of buoyancy' in order to preserve stability.

I have to thank public libraries for providing books without number before I could afford to buy my own. I still recall the pleasure and excitement of reading as a schoolboy H.G. Wells's *First Men on the Moon* and *The War of the Worlds* – my first books from a public library and the opening of a marvellous new world for a youngster to explore.

It was a book from a public library that had a profound influence on my choice of a career – as indeed it had on at least two other youngsters who in later life became Presidents of the Institution of Electrical Engineers. The book was *The Boy Electrician* by Morgan and Carpenter, first published in 1920 – it showed schoolboys how to make electric motors, telephones and the like from scrap materials, and, more importantly, how to make simple electrical measuring equipment. (See Part 1, Chapter 1.)

My earlier contact with Wells led on to my reading as a teenager his sociological novels such as *Kipps* and *Ann Veronica* that helped towards an understanding of the adult world into which I was growing. I have recounted in Part 1 how, when I was an apprentice in Portsmouth Dockyard, the recommendation of a Dockyard schoolmaster Mr McKenzie led me to choose as a prize Galsworthy's *Forsyte Saga* – the three volumes of which I still have and which has been read and re-read not only by myself but also members of my family. This book, like Wells's novels, helped a youngster to expand his horizons beyond his immediate circle.

During my apprenticeship days in the late 1920s, sound radio broadcasting was getting into its stride and provided interesting talks by scientists and engineers as well as politicians and novelists. These talks were often reproduced in written form in the BBC journal *The Listener* – to which I subscribed regularly out of my meagre apprenticeship pay. I can still picture myself reading *The Listener* whilst munching my lunchtime sandwiches, tucked away in the spotting-top at the mast head of the ill-fated battle-cruiser *HMS Hood*!

I must mention a book that had a major impact on my choice of the Post Office instead of the Admiralty for my future career after leaving college (Chapter 4, Part 1). It was Erich Maria Remarque's *All Quiet on the Western Front* which has been described as:

'...a grimly realistic work, depicting with relentless clarity and warm compassion the sufferings, courage and comradeship of the common soldiers, and embodying a bitter condemnation of militarism, which became one of the most widely-read novels of all time.'

[Encarta Encyclopedia CD]

All through my life reading has provided relaxation as well as information – it included science fiction by A.C. Clarke (of communication satellite and *Odyssey 2001* fame) and the American master Asimov. A favourite author in a different field has been Patrick O'Brian, whose fictional stories of the British Navy in Napoleonic times, when the Navy was wooden-hulled and square-rigged, remind me vividly of the life that my sail-maker grandfather must have lived. The novels are remarkable, not only for the vivid characterisation of the principal players Captain Jack Aubrey and his surgeon/Admiralty intelligence officer Stephen Maturin, but also the immense erudition and realistic detail – including that of the natural world – that O'Brian brings to his accounts of sea-battles and voyaging around the world.

I have enjoyed too the novels of Nevile Shute, partly for their authentic engineering flavour. One of them, *Point of No Return*, was strangely prophetic about metal fatigue as a cause of wing failure and disasters in flight of the first jet aircraft. Since I had crossed the Atlantic in an early Comet – before it was known as a cause of failure in that marvellous pioneering aircraft – this book has had for me a special interest.

Many other authors have given me hours of enjoyable reading – from Jane Austen, Anthony Trollope and Thomas Hardy at one pole to Jack Higgins and John le Carré at another. Some day I'd like to be able to thank them all!

Writing

The Baconian edict has it that 'Reading maketh a full man, writing an exact man'; the discipline of writing requires the writer to gather together his ideas or views, present them logically and clearly, and be prepared to defend them if they are criticised.

School projects and college theses required a good deal of writing, but it was the profession of research that involved writing at a high level of precision, for example in research proposals, progress reports and final reports on what had been achieved. And if the results of the research justified it, there were scientific or engineering papers to be prepared for submission to professional bodies such as the Institution of Electrical Engineers, which had to run the guantlet of approval by critical referees before they were published. At the PO Radio and Research Branches my mentors, and strictest critics of report writing, were my chiefs Captain C.F. Booth and Albert Mumford, later Sir Albert and Engineer-in-Chief; their frequent requests 'to make it clearer', 'avoid unnecessary words' or 'rewrite in shorter form' at first caused much anguish, but the end results were much better. Even now I can sense them leaning over my shoulder and giving good advice!

Over the years my writing output has included, in addition to many professional reports, a considerable collection of articles for technical journals, drafts for talks and letters to the press (including one in *The Times* on the problems foreseen in privatisation of the national telecommunication system; I'm told this was more due to good luck than judgement, since the going success rate for letters in *The Times* was about one published for ten offered!). The drafts for talks to clubs and societies included topics such as 'The Mysterious Universe' and 'How to Lose Your Wife at Sea Without Actually Trying' (this reflected my sailing hobby and an amusing misadventure – see Part 3, Chapter 3). And there were the poems that formed part of my more private personal life.

With retirement came time to reflect and write at leisure, from which came first my *Memoirs of a Telecommunications Engineer*, published in 1978, 350 copies of which were printed in paperback by a local (Woodbridge) printer, and sold at the modest price of £7 from my home address, mainly to people in British Telecom. Very few copies now remain, and it is pleasing to note that income from sales covered the costs of printing by a small margin. Written soon after retirement, when memories of people and events were still fresh, it provided a helpful source for my second book, *The Communications Miracle*, published by Plenum of London and New York in 1995.

The Communications Miracle was a much more ambitious attempt to trace the history of telecommunications from the Victorian scientists and mathematicians who laid the foundations, to the pioneers whose innovations created, step-by-step, one of the greatest of the human artefacts – today's worldwide telecommunication and broadcasting systems. A primary aim in writing the book was to identify the pioneers whose work in technology – the invention of transistors and the microchip, digital techniques, optical fibre cables and communication satellites – had made possible the Internet and the World-Wide Web. By focusing on the human element I hoped that the book might inspire some of today's young people to seek careers in information technology, communications research and engineering.

Preparation of the book involved some six years of research, much helped by staff at the BT Laboratories Library, Martlesham, and BT Archives, London. And my American friend of Telstar days, Dr Gene O'Neill, Editor of the *History of Science and Engineering in the Bell System* was a most helpful critic and adviser.

But the finding of an English publisher at first proved difficult – time and again the response was 'An interesting read but does not quite fit our present catalogue'! By good fortune an enterprising young man, Alistair Layzell, living in a neighbouring village to mine and with a good background in the publishing industry, had set up as a freelance publicist for books and the media, well equipped with fax and computer facilities. Within a month he had found my ideal publisher – Plenum of New York and London – whose London Editor, Ken Derham, gave the book a warm welcome. Within a short time the necessary legal arrangements as to royalties and copyright were concluded and we were off.

From my point of view the arrangement with Plenum was

ideal – a substantial part of the book reflected American contributions to communications technology – notably from the Bell Laboratories – about which I was well informed from both professional contacts in joint UK–USA projects and from my sabbatical year in the USA. And of course it added the American market to the British market for book sales!

The formal launch of the book in the UK took place, appropriately enough, in the John Bray Lecture Theatre at the BT Laboratories, Martlesham, in December 1995, with some kind contributions from Sir Iain Vallance, Chairman of the BT Board, and his Deputy, Dr Alan Rudge, delivered from his London office by video link and large-screen projection in the Lecture Theatre.

Finally, after many years of practising it, some general comments on the art of writing may be appropriate.

Writing does a great deal to clarify thought and make it precise, a quality that is sometimes absent in the spoken word. On the other hand, the spoken word is undoubtedly capable of carrying a greater emotional charge through the emphasis the voice can give. Perhaps it is significant that Sir Winston Churchill's most effective 'impromptu' speeches in the House of Commons were often the result of careful written preparation beforehand!

I believe that the computer with its visual display in typescript of the words and sentences tapped out on the keyboard is a considerable aid to better writing, as compared with handwritten text. The display on the PC is an invitation to consider what has been written, and to rephrase and reposition where necessary; while this is still possible with handwritten text, it is cumbersome to do so and the end result is untidy unless completely rewritten. The facility of the PC to produce well laid-out text in a directly publishable form is of course a further bonus.

Poetry

I have long been fascinated by poetry, especially by its ability to record and recall emotion more vividly than straight prose. It was this characteristic that made me, from time to time and when impelled by the beauty of a scene, the pangs of unrequited love or the anguish of the loss of a near one, to scribble a poem in a private notebook. One poem – 'Night on Walton Channel', which for me is very evocative of my sailing days – follows this page; others are presented in latter chapters. It is signed by 'Byron Haj' – which may be recognised as an anagram of my name, but nothing to do of course with *the Byron*!

My 'poems' were not compiled with any real knowledge of the formal nature of poetry, iambic structure or rhythm; true, I could distinguish between rhyme and blank verse, and generally used the latter for its greater freedom of expression. In this I was probably reassured by the fact that all of Shakespeare, except the sonnets, was in blank verse. It was not until recently that I discovered from my computer and the *Encarta* CD encyclopedia, what a complicated business 'real' poetry is, with its iambic trimeters and tetrameters and stanzas; had I known earlier, I doubt whether I would have been so bold as to try to write poetry at all!

Night on Walton Channel

Two days in Autumn
the sky an azure blue,
a gentle wind
and a calm sea.

Out from Orwell river,
sailing barges and yachts,
sails dark against a silver, sparkling sea.

And on past buoys of odd names,
'Pye End', 'Crab Knoll' and 'High Tower',
to the peaceful haven of the Walton Channel.

At anchor,
the setting sun glorious in the Western sky,
and sea birds feeding at water's edge.

To match the scene,
on ship's radio,
a Greig pianoforte concerto,
and later a voice saying:
'women of men do poets make,
and children-philosophers'.

At midnight,
the river flowing silently, mirror-like,
a sharp-edged moon and stars,
the vast vault of the sky
in the water brilliantly reflected.

The lights of Felixstowe and Harwich,
a line on far horizon,
sparkling like diamonds.

The sea birds silent now,
but a golden owl,
with large and luminous eyes,
flies by with scarce-heard sweep of wings.

This quiet world of water and reedy islands
in sharp contrast to the vastness
and unimaginable complexity of space.

Wherein are found:
strange 'pulsars' that beat out
the mechanical clock of the universe,
'quasars', more powerful by far
than the largest nuclear bomb,
'black holes' where light itself
is confined by gravity,
and time reverses.

And one wonders,
wherein this vastness lies God,
and the souls of those
one has loved and lost.

Byron Haj

114

The English class at Portsmouth Southern Secondary School must have introduced me to some poetry that made a strong impression – I can still, without referring to a text and after some 70 years, hear myself as a youngster in front of the class, declaiming in a pseudo-strident voice, the famous lines from Shakespeare's *Henry V* at the battle of Agincourt:

'Once more unto the breach dear friends,
or close the wall up with our English dead.
In peace there's nothing so becomes a man
as modest stillness and humility.
But when the blast of war sounds in your ears
then imitate the action of the tiger.
Stiffen the sinews, summon up the blood,
disguise fair nature with hard-favoured rage.
Let the eye pry through the portal of the head,
and the brow o'erwhelm it,
as fearfully as doth the galled rock
o'erhang and jutty the confounded ocean.'

One of my favourite poets was John Betjeman, whose blank verse poems so evocatively recreated scenes from his childhood in Cornwall, schooldays at Marlborough School, his home at Highgate and localities around the 'new' Metropolitan Railway such as Cricklewood and Gladstone Park, these having a special resonance for me as reminders of my early PO days at Dollis Hill. By a quite remarkable coincidence my daughter Frances gave me, as a birthday present, a copy of Betjeman's *Summoned by Bells* almost at the same time as Gilbert Metson, my predecessor as Director of Research at Dollis Hill, was given by his daughter, without collusion with mine, a copy of the same book!

115

2

Love, Marriage and Children

Courting Days

Looking back over some 65 years to visualise oneself as a very normal, heterosexual young male, driven by that mysterious instinct that has ensured the continuity of the human race, is a fascinating but somewhat daunting experience. Of course I was much attracted to most of the girls of my own age group who came within my orbit of acquaintance. However, one in particular – my wife Margaret – had evidently made an impression that resulted in a rewarding marriage that has lasted more than 60 years.

Margaret was the only daughter of Fred and Mary Earp; he had joined the Royal Navy as an Engine Room Artificer at the same time as my father, a few years before the outbreak of the First World War at a time when work was hard to come by. The two men became firm friends, sharing common experiences and the hazards of the sea war. My mother and Mary Earp, a delightful Welsh lady, had much in common; they shared the anxieties that arose from husbands who were away at sea sometimes for a year or more. Living in the same part of Portsmouth, it was perhaps inevitable that Margaret and I too should become good friends. There is a family story that, when Mary was pregnant with Margaret, my mother commiserated with her, not knowing that she too was pregnant (with me, as it happened). And so Margaret's and my birthdays are only a few weeks apart.

When my friendship with Margaret blossomed into courtship, I was still at college. Much of the courting was done during college vacations, some of it with the help of an AJS motorbike with Margaret as pillion passenger. It was an enjoyable time, with trips to Dorset and the New Forest. There was too a visit to an uncle and aunt of mine in Ulster, of which I recall an excursion by train (shared with a Sunday School outing of the 'Wee Frees'), to the lovely Mountains of Mourne.

However, the course of true love never runs smoothly and there were the occasional tiffs and on one occasion a break 'to part for ever'. During the latter I became friendly with Margaret's best friend Caroline – who kindly typed my Master of Science thesis and was my companion for a time on country walks and theatre visits. But Margaret and I met again, seemingly by chance, and realised that we were well suited to become life partners.

Marriage

And so it was that in April 1936 we were married in St Mary's Church, Southsea, an event that gave both sets of parents, as well as ourselves, much pleasure.

Our honeymoon was spent in Paris on a rather cold Easter, travelling by train and boat via Newhaven and Dieppe, after a rapturous send-off by a group of friends from Portsmouth Town Station. We seem to have spent some of it wandering about on guided tours of the Catacombs, with their piles of skulls and bones, and the Paris Sewer System (which was fortunately much more hygienic than one might have expected). There were visits to the top of the Eiffel Tower, dinner on a *bateau mouche* on the River Seine, and of course visits to museums and art galleries. And I can still recall with pleasure the glorious taste and fragrance of real French coffee, served in a man-size bowl with warm, crisp croissants.

And 50 years later, on our Golden Wedding anniversary, we again visited Paris. Nothing much seemed to have changed – except the shoulder-high free 'pissoirs' in the streets, which had been replaced by computer-controlled coin-operated toilets.

First Home

By the summer of 1936 I had completed my Probationary Training as a Post Office Assistant Engineer, had a career ahead of me and a starting salary of £60 a month. And, as recounted in Chapter 1, Part 1, my first post was in the Experimental Radio Branch of the PO Engineering Department at Dollis Hill, a posting that pleased me very much.

Those were the days when a deposit of £25 and a sizeable mortgage, backed by a secure job, enabled one to buy for £1,000 a modest bungalow – in our case overlooking fields leading down to the Welsh Harp at Hendon, with the PO Research Station on a hill across the lake. My home was fortunately within easy bicycling distance of Dollis Hill – a car was not financially possible for several years. This is in marked contrast with today, when even young men at college expect a car as of right.

Margaret and I were the first 'young marrieds' of a group of half a dozen of my colleagues who had joined the PO at the same time. They became our friends, and our home an informal visiting place for these young men and their girlfriends. Those first years were very happy ones, with much fun, parties and weekend walks in the countryside around the Chiltern Hills.

Looking back over the years, one has observed with interest that the marriages of those friends proved a good deal more stable and durable than in many other walks of life – perhaps because our interesting and demanding careers left little time or energy for extra-marital activities!

Life During the War

The outbreak of war in 1939 changed our lives markedly, as it did for everyone else. The area in which we were living, Hendon and Kingsbury, had its share of the London bombing, and we were visited by both the V2 rocket bombs and, in some ways more terrifying, the V1 flying 'buzz' bombs. We were provided, in the street outside our bungalow, with a brick-built shelter that did more for morale than provide real protection. It was damp and cold most of the time, and was only used when bombing was particularly intense.

Much safer and more convenient to use was an indoor Anderson shelter built of iron sheet and girders that came later in the war period. However, in 1941 Margaret became pregnant and for safety moved to Otley, a few miles from Leeds, where happily she was able to stay with a PO colleague and his wife. It was here that our first daughter, Frances, was born – as it happened, on the only occasion when a nearby anti-aircraft gun battery had to be brought into action against a German bomber!

When my wartime activities for the PO Radio Experimental Branch permitted I travelled occasionally to Leeds to see my wife and first-born daughter – usually standing in blacked-out trains packed with troops. However, as the tide of war on the Continent moved eastward and the bombing of London eased, it became possible and reasonably safe for Margaret and daughter Frances to return to London and our home by the Welsh Harp. I remember our first Christmas together as a family in wartime, when every relative and friend gave baby Frances a soft cuddly toy!

The Postwar Years

To our great joy, in March 1945 another daughter, Elizabeth, was born. With a growing family we began to think about a larger home than our bungalow by the Welsh Harp could provide, and as the hazards of war receded we looked for a house not too far from Dollis Hill. This we found on Barn Hill, near Wembley Park – in a locality popular with stage and broadcasting people because it offered ready access to London and the West End via the Metropolitan Railway. We bought the house from a West End nightclub singer and her dance-band husband; we got quite used to being invited on the telephone to come and perform long after they had gone! As

119

neighbours we had Millicent Martin, Benny Green and Steve Race, so we felt almost part of the entertainment world.

Frances, and later Elizabeth, attended the local (state) school at Fryent, Kingsbury, where, with good and kindly teachers, they made good progress.

Frances passed the entrance examination for, and continued her education at, the grant-aided North London Collegiate School – a school with a fine record of scholastic achievement, good discipline and a well-balanced view of education, under the direction of a remarkable Headmistress, Dame Kitty Anderson. Elizabeth too was all set to join her sister at the North London Collegiate School when events took a sad turn that threw a dark shadow over all our lives.

Loss of a Daughter

Elizabeth – Liz – was a bright and cheerful child, with an engaging personality and a sense of fun. She was fond of reading – perhaps inherited from her maternal grandmother, via her father! And at 11 years of age she had begun to show an ability to write, sometimes in poetic form. Her great love, like so many young girls, was for horses, and she longed for us one day to live in the country where she could have one of her own. But it was not to be.

School medical examinations had diagnosed a degree of progressive spinal curvature, and a Consultant at the Great Ormond Street Hospital for Children advised an operation to correct the curvature before spina bifida occurred. The decision to do so was made shortly after Margaret and I had returned from my sabbatical year in the USA. We had just another month together with Liz in the summer of 1956 – she was then 11 years old. I can still visualise Liz romping with her Golden Cocker Spaniel, Punch, in the park on Barn Hill.

Prior to the operation Liz kept a diary in the hospital, that began with the words:

'I Elizabeth Bray came into the Royal National Ortho-

120

paedic Hospital on the 18th of July 1956, on a cause of a crooked spine. First I was in a plaster jacket, then in an iron framework; then after 14 months would be free to do what I liked.
'Giving thanks to Sister, Staff and the Nurses and specially to my Parents who encouraged me.'

Liz's diary is full of cheerful chat and jokes with girls in her ward and the visitors who came to see her. It also contains references to the preparations for her operation, which shows she had a realistic view of what had to be done.

Sadly, she died soon after the operation on 26 August 1956. It was many months before her parents' and sister's grief had eased; her Cocker Spaniel was inconsolable.

As I write this I see on the window sill of my study the small wooden horse I brought back for her from America. Perhaps the poem 'Arnold 7966' I wrote in her memory will be some small tribute to a much-loved and unique child. (Arnold 7966 was the telephone number of our home on Barn Hill.)

Arnold 7966

Across half a life time
I hear, crystal clear, a child's voice,
speaking from home to my office,
'Arnold 7966 – who's calling?'

Our daughter Elizabeth,
who died at eleven years
in Stanmore Hospital, after an operation
to correct her sadly curved spine.

She was a lovely, intelligent child,
with understanding beyond her years.
She loved horses and poetry,
these poems appeared in her hospital diary:

121

'In School'
'I used to go to a bright school,
where youth and frolic taught in turn.
But idle scholar that I was,
I liked to play and would not learn.
So the Great Teacher did ordain
that I should try the School of Pain.'

'Thanks'
'I thank You for so many things,
that had I made a list,
there would still be a hundred more
a happy child had missed.
So make me always thankful Lord,
though I am lost for words,
to thank You for my home,
my garden and the song of birds.'

Byron Haj

3

We Move to East Anglia

Our home on Barn Hill, Wembley Park, had served us well from the early 1950s; it was conveniently placed for Dollis Hill and the girls were happily settled in their schools. But by the late 1960s the character of the neighbourhood had changed, and not for the better. A large new estate had been created at nearby Chalkhill, mainly to accommodate people who had been moved from London. The incidence of burglaries in the Barn Hill neighbourhood increased, and there were unprecedented cases of personal violence. The Wembley Park Council became Brent Council, and a Labour majority took over. There were strikes that involved the teachers at the local schools and others that interrupted the refuse collections. So it was not unwelcome that in 1973 it became necessary for us to consider a move.

Once the move of the PO Laboratories from Dollis Hill to Martlesham was well in hand, albeit in temporary accommodation, it became desirable for myself, as Director of Research, to move there part-time, whilst continuing to maintain a base at Dollis Hill. This involved, for a time, having two homes – one the family home at Barn Hill and a new one that had to be located not too far from Martlesham. Fortunately we (Margaret and I, for our daughter had by then married) were able to rent for a time a house owned by a PO Director of Finance, in the pleasant and friendly village of Earl Soham, Suffolk. The house (more a small baronial hall!) provided much roomier accommodation than we really needed, but was excellent for holding parties with friends. This admirable arrangement enabled us to look around for a

123

permanent home without being pressed to make an early decision.

After a search period of some months we found in 1974 a very convenient detached house with half an acre of garden in the village of Bredfield, about five miles north-west of Woodbridge, Suffolk – that became our new home, at least until the writing of this autobiography in 1997/8!

Bredfield proved an excellent choice, for it is a village with a great community spirit and one in which we made many friends. It was here that I began to learn about the problems of the rural economy and the work of Local Community, Parish, District and County Councils. And there was a new village hall, with a purpose-built voluntarily-run shop extension, to be built – with which I inevitably became involved in retirement.

The neighbouring small town, Woodbridge, on the Deben River, is a delightful place – providing for all the basic shopping needs together with good medical facilities, first-class restaurants, a community hall, public library and several bookshops. In past years barges sailing along the North Sea shore with cargoes of grain, coal and timber moored at quays in Woodbridge, and today there are thriving sailing clubs and shipyards.

The move from the somewhat claustrophobic, built-up environment of Wembley Park to the open skies and gently undulating countryside of Suffolk was a revelation and an education in itself. For the first time one was seeing marvellous sunrises and sunsets, and the star-lit sky at night, in all their true glory. And it was good to live in a thriving rural community where farmers were producing excellent vegetables and meat, and fish was to be had straight from the North Sea.

My sailing hobby didn't suffer – there were fascinating new sailing areas around the Orwell, Stour, Orde and Deben Rivers, and the Walton Channel, to explore. I have to admit, however, that unkind 'friends' have been known to assert that the choice of Martlesham for the new PO Research Centre was influenced by the Director with this sailing facility in mind. However, the North Sea, in the shape of my favourite beach at

Shingle Street, was a shade cooler than I would have preferred for swimming!

Bredfield has its own historian, Mrs Val Norrington, who brought to my notice a fascinating piece of local history involving my name. The 1838 Tithe map shows a field not a hundred yards from my home in Bredfield called 'The Brays'. Further research in the Seckford Collection at Woodbridge Library revealed the following information about taxes paid on the value of land or goods:

Year 1524. To Henry VIIIth, in the 15th year of his reign, from Bredfield in the County of Suffolk:
William Bray, 'in goods of £10'.........15s.0d
John Bray, 'in goods of 20 marks'....£1.0s.0d

Year 1568. To Elizabeth 1,...'levy on movable goods and lands':
John Bray, 'in lands of £8'.................10s.8d.

How strange that, in 1974, we should have settled next door to my exact namesakes of some 450 years ago!

4

A Sailing Hobby

Almost from my teenage days sailing has been an important part of my life – no doubt stimulated by the family links with the Royal Navy and my apprenticeship in Portsmouth Naval Dockyard. But it was undoubtedly my sail-maker grandfather, William James Bray, and his life on the square-rigged ships of the 1880s Royal Navy that inspired my own love of wooden ships and sail.

My first teenage experiments with sail were made in ramshackle, and somewhat leaky, dinghies with lug sails that could be hired for pennies at Milton Lock, Portsmouth, for sailing in Langstone Harbour. Fortunately, my parents were blissfully unaware of the hazards that this entailed from the fast tidal currents that flowed in and out of Langstone Harbour!

Later, as an apprentice in Portsmouth Dockyard I had, with my fellow apprentices, the privilege of using a ship's whaler to row in Portsmouth Harbour and across to the Isle of Wight. This was hard work, sometimes against adverse tides, and I longed for my own boat under sail.

My first boat, bought in 1966, was a delightful centre-cockpit, 28ft long, cold-moulded ply sloop designed by Illing-worth-Primrose, called *Kareela III* (Kareela is Australian aborigine for 'West Wind'). She was moored at the Marina in Chichester Harbour, from where we – that is Margaret, daughter Frances and son-in-law Brian – made our early ventures under sail, at first exploring Bosham Creek and the mooring at East Head, Hayling Island, and then, greatly venturing, to the Isle of Wight at Bembridge and Seaview.

We learned a great deal about seamanship from *Kareela*, not the least was how lively a modern 'short-keel' boat like *Kareela* could be in turbulent seas such as we often encountered on the sand bar at the entrance to Chichester Harbour when an outgoing 5-knot tide had a stiff south-wester gale blowing over it!

My next boat, named in Norwegian *Sjøhest* for 'Seahorse', bought in 1969 from her first owner. She was a Norwegian Troll motor-sailor that had appeared in the Olympia Boat Show in 1966. Her hull, built at Bergen, is basic Norwegian fishing boat design – clinker built of pine planks on oak frames – with lines going back to the Viking long-ships (and, incidentally, which reappeared in the Saxon treasure ship discovered at Sutton Hoo, a few miles from where I now live).

Sjøhest is sloop-rigged, 32 ft overall and 9.5 ft beam; she has a canoe stern and a long keel. The latter gives her much greater stability in a rough sea than her short-keel predecessor *Kareela*. Her modest sail area of some 300 sq ft and wide beam make her easy to handle, even in rough weather. The roomy interior is finished in solid mahogany with chart table, dining table and bunks for six people. She is powered by a Perkins 4107 marinised diesel engine, water-cooled via a heat exchanger and circulating sea water. (See plates 14 and 15)

Not surprisingly in view of my professional interests, I had equipped *Sjøhest* with long- and medium-wave radio transmitters and receivers, a multi-channel VHF marine radio transmitter/receiver for safety, calling and ship-shore telephone communication.

There was also a crossed-loop MF radio-direction finder, a digital echo-sounder and a speed/distance log operated from a miniature propeller outside the hull. Although this was long before the days of satellite navigation, we felt that with this equipment we could find our way about the seas, call the coastguard and get help if trouble arose.

This boat became part of my life for nearly 20 years, and to it I owe not only the pleasure of sailing with family and friends, but a real contribution to physical and mental health. There is nothing like sailing and having to cope with the immediate hazards of wind and tide to banish for a time the problems of one's professional life. And even the maintenance work – of which there is ample on a wooden boat! – was a good therapy in itself.

Throughout this period I kept a boat log, recording in addition to details of voyages in *Sjøhest* and her various crew members, notes of maintenance work and changes of equipment made from time to time. It is remarkable how the brief notes made in the log recall the people, the pleasure and fun, and the occasional dangers encountered in the past. Perhaps a summary here of a few of the voyages will serve as reminders.

From 1969 to 1973 *Sjøhest* was based on a pontoon mooring in Chichester Marina; the Marina was accessed via a lock, the gates of which had to be operated on entering and leaving except for an hour or so at high water, when 'free flow' prevailed. The Marina provided a companionable yacht club and dry-land maintenance facilities. It proved a good location from which to pursue a sailing career – even though it meant an hour-and-a-half car drive from our home at Wembley Park. In those days the yachts in the Marina were numbered in hundreds as compared with today's thousands, which made transiting the lock much easier. It also meant that the Harbour was far less congested and sailing less hazardous.

Our first voyages were in Chichester Harbour itself, exploring Bosham Creek and occasionally mooring for a weekend stay off the sandy beaches of East Head at Hayling Island. Then, growing more adventurous and having crossed the shipping lanes of the Solent, there were pleasant harbourages to explore around the Isle of Wight – including Bembridge and its tide-mill, Cowes and the Royal Yacht Club, and Yarmouth at the eastern end of the island.

One pleasing adventure was the day when Margaret and I circumnavigated the Isle of Wight on our own, starting from the Newtown River just East of Cowes (where else could you pay for your mooring fee with a National Trust membership card?). Then sailing on to the Needles on a falling tide, and, having carefully judged the tides, rounding the Needles in sunshine and a calm sea, and gliding on along the southern

128

shore of the island on a rising, west-flowing tide and a following wind. At the western end of the island the tide was turning again and we sailed blissfully on to Bembridge and a comfortable overnight mooring in the Harbour. Columbus himself could not have been more satisfied with his navigation!

Not all our visits to the Isle of Wight were free from hazard. There was one occasion when, after a visit to Bembridge, I missed a gale warning for the day when we were due to return to Chichester. All was well until we left the lea of the Isle of Wight and approached the entrance to Chichester Harbour where the south-west gale, blowing over the out-flowing tide, had whipped-up mountainous seas over the Bar. We lost the Avon inflatable dinghy with its Chrysler outboard motor, which was being towed, and we never saw it again.

More peaceful was a visit to Poole Harbour and Pottery Pier off Brownsea Island, with its lovely views of the Dorset coast and Corfe Castle. Peaceful, that is, until disturbed by the mating calls of the numerous peacocks on Brownsea Island. And of course, true to form, we ran aground on a sand bank in Poole Harbour and found the largest cockles we had ever seen!

A voyage to the West Country and Dartmouth had its interesting moments, for instance, in passing the Army firing range at Lulworth, Dorset, we were met by a Naval launch and diverted out to sea and eventually into a fog bank.The ship's radio DF came into action and we successfully homed on to the Shambles Light Vessel, and from there groped our way on a reciprocal bearing in dense fog towards Portland Bill. I could see nothing until my son-in-law said: 'Look up, Dad, aren't those cottages up there?' And so it was, we were actually under the lea of Portland Bill; a little more guidance from our depth sounder and we were safe in Weymouth Harbour.

Perhaps the most exciting voyage was a crossing of the English Channel, from Chichester to Cherbourg, in May 1971 with Margaret and friends Marion and Cyril Floyd. This was an overnight sail that required some interesting dead-reckoning navigation to allow for the changing tides in the Channel. There was too a need to keep clear of shipping in mid-Channel and the fishing boats off the coast of France. My relief when, in the grey light of dawn, we saw the lighthouse at Cape Levi, not far from Cherbourg, was immense and greeted with a rather early 'splicing of the mainbrace'!

In Cherbourg Yacht Club we met and enjoyed the company of Howard Steele, then Chief Engineer of ITA, who had a Troll similar to mine, and Dr Broadway, Director of Research of EMI, who also had sailed from England.

From Cherbourg we sailed on, this time accompanied by our daughter Frances and son-in-law Brian, to visit Guernsey and Alderney, braving the 30ft rise and fall of tide, the fast tidal currents and the hidden reefs along the Normandy coast. However, after leaving Alderney on our return to England we encountered a south-west gale and very stormy seas as we approached the English coast in the gloom of evening. Frances had been seasick, so I decided to seek the shelter and relative calm of a mooring in Swanage Bay for the night.

By the following morning the weather had improved, and Margaret and Frances decided to make their way by train from Swanage to the Marina at Lymington, where Brian and I would meet them with *Sjøhest*. After saying fond farewells to our now happy wives, Brian and I sailed on – only to realise when they were out of sight that we had, unfortunately, left them at Shanklin in the Isle of Wight, instead of Swanage in Dorset!

For an account of the fascinating and hilarious consequences that flowed from this, I thought, rather trivial error, the reader might refer to *Yachting Monthly*[1] where the full story appears under the title of 'John Bray Makes 30-mile Navigational Error (and Loses and Finds his Wife)'.

Following my move to East Anglia in 1973, a PO colleague Harold Stanesby and I sailed *Sjøhest* from Chichester Marina to a berth in the then new marina at Levington on the River Orwell, Suffolk. This was an interesting voyage, involving crossing the Thames estuary in fog at right angles to the busy shipping lanes, by 'hopping' from buoy to buoy. And what sheer joy it was to find that there was just sufficient water in the Swin Spitway, between the Buxey and Gunfleet Sands off the Essex coast, to let Sjøhest through!

Although it was with some regret that one left the yachting mecca of the Isle of Wight and the Solent, exploring the East Coast rivers Orwell, Stour, Deben and Ore/Alde brought a new kind of sailing experience, described for example by Maurice Griffiths in his book *The Magic of the Swatchways*[2] and Arthur Ransome in *Secret Waters*[3], and which I have tried to reflect in the poem 'Night on Walton Channel' (Chapter 1, Part 3).

Eventually I gave up the relatively expensive pontoon berth in Levington Marina for a much cheaper swinging berth on a buoy in the Deben River – thanks to the kindly Harbour Master George Collins whom I used to meet (and occasionally buy a Scotch to go with his Adnams) in the delightful Ramsholt Arms. True, one had to use a dinghy to get to and from one's boat, but a swinging mooring on the river was so much nearer the heart of sailing – the quietness enabled one to hear the songs of the seabirds, while the peaceful lapping of waves on the clinker hull was a powerful inducement to sleep on board.

My ownership of *Sjøhest* came to an end in 1987, when advancing years and 'frozen' shoulder muscles made it difficult to haul in the anchor chain or tighten the main sheet in a stiff breeze. So she was sold and sailed by her new owner on the Thames for a time. But recently (1997) she has been fully refitted at Woodbridge, and it is good to see my companion of nearly 20 years, and many sea miles, return to her former state of glory.

5

Some Ideas Not Yet Realised

Being of a somewhat imaginative turn of mind – and having lived in an atmosphere of research that requires one to look beyond the visible horizon – it is perhaps not remarkable that, from time to time, ideas occur to one that involve new technology concepts or possible improvements in ways of doing things.There follows an account of some of these that seem worthy of rescuing from the correspondence files that announced their birth and recorded their (possibly premature) decease.

The Personal TV-Video Receiver

The idea that there could be a visual analogue of the popular audio-cassette/headphone receiver occurred to me – as it may well have to others – in 1982. By incorporating a miniature TV screen and a lens in spectacles the viewer could be offered a new and potentially superior mode of viewing:

- by excluding all external visual distraction, he would be literally 'in the picture'
- virtual large screen presentation at low cost
- three-dimensional viewing, since each eye sees a separate picture

I wrote a memorandum on this concept and its commercial potential in 1984 and offered it to Sir Clive Sinclair as one of UK's 'ideas men', suggesting that 'we should not leave it all to

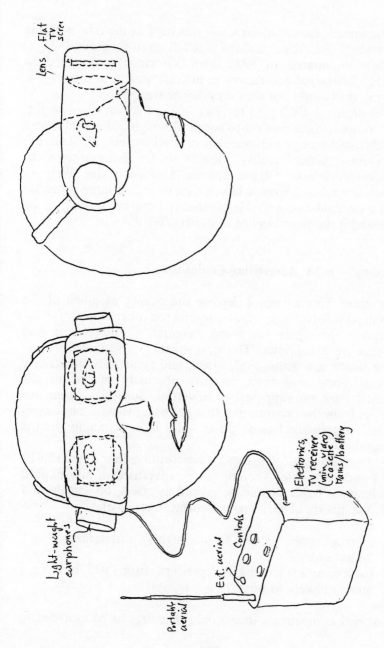

Lens / Flat TV screen

Light-weight earphones

Portable aerial

Ext. aerial

Controls

Electronics, TV receiver (min. video cassette) trans/battery

Personal TV-video receiver

133

the Japanese'. However, Sir Clive was busy at the time with his three-wheel electric car and the idea fell on stony ground.

Sony, announced in 1992 their 'Visortron' - designed to provide individual passengers in aircraft with a means of TV viewing that would not distract other passengers.

The personal TV/Video receiver in a convenient lightweight, easy-to-use format, has yet to come, although today's advances in micro-technology indicate that it is achievable. Incidentally, the clumsy 'virtual reality' viewers so far demonstrated on *Tomorrow's World* TV are not the kind of device likely to attract a market. I have a hunch that there is a large potential public demand and a viable commercial market waiting to be exploited if the right kind of device is offered.

'Adcomp' – a TV Advertising Competition

Like many TV viewers, I deplore the quality of much of the commercial advertising that appears on our screens, whilst admitting that there are some imaginative, entertaining and informative exceptions. The poor-quality advertisements are those which are 'gimmicky', brash, and sometimes offensively violent. They may even be only obscurely related to the product they are supposed to advertise. Such advertisements distract from the programmes that are being viewed, but unfortunately the public has no direct voice in determining what is acceptable.

Some years ago I suggested a competition (not approved by ITA) under the title 'Adcomp' to be advertised in newspapers, in which the public would be invited to assess, on a scale of 1 to 5, the quality of each advertisement in terms of:

- entertainment value, from 'highly entertaining' to 'objectionable'
- success in advertising the product, from 'will buy' to 'most unlikely to buy'

To attract competitors there could be prizes to be awarded to those whose overall numerical assessments of a group of advertisements most closely corresponded to the national statistical average response.

For the advertisers there would be a much more realistic appreciation of the response of the public to their efforts – including the strengths and weaknesses of the adverts – than could possibly be achieved by straw polls involving limited numbers of viewers.

Will More Channels Mean Better TV?
The Fallacy and a Solution
(based on an article written in June 1997)

Television viewers are being offered more and more channels – 30 digital 'over-the-air' broadcasting channels and 200 or more by Sky TV satellites, in addition to five existing TV broadcasting channels and perhaps 100 or more on cable TV. Powerful commercial and advertising interests are competing for control of the new channels, but there has been no public debate on whether these developments are in the best interests of the viewing public.

To fill some hundreds of additional TV channels up to 24 hours a day, year after year, will require a vast proliferation of new video programme material. But the talent and originality – and even the finance – available to create these new programmes is finite. More and more will rely on advertising – with its adverse effect on viewer satisfaction. The average quality of the programmes will necessarily suffer, and the bad will tend to drive out the good – in a modern version of Gresham's Law.

Technology advance now offers every prospect of a new approach based on electronic video libraries offering 'view what you want, when you want' access to an unrestricted library of recorded video programmes – including such things as news items and sport events within minutes of the actual event, and newly-released films and plays.

The viewer's choice could be made via a 'user-friendly' menu displayed on his TV screen and a simple numerical keyboard. Or, for the more sophisticated user, access could be provided via a 'multi-media set-top keyboard' giving access to electronic shopping, banking, and information services via the Internet.

'View-on-demand' TV would be essentially a 'pay-as-you-view' service in which the viewer pays for the item viewed as he would for a film in a cinema or a play in the theatre.

This has the advantage that the financial return to the programme producer is directly related to the number of viewers – which creates a strong incentive to produce high-quality programmes.

View-on-demand TV could be provided over existing telephone wires to the home (as BT field trials have demonstrated), or over modified cable networks. The new millimetric-wave 'Ionica' local area telephone system, with its small rooftop aerials, would also be suitable. However, satellite TV and 'over-the-air' broadcasting would not be suitable because of the large numbers of different frequencies needed to provide the many channels from the electronic video library to viewers' homes.

A large-scale 'view-on-demand', 'pay-as-you-go' TV service with well-equipped electronic video libraries could offer substantial advantages to the viewer:

- the convenience of being able to view a chosen TV programme exactly when he wishes to do so
- a real and immediate choice from an unrestricted range of TV programmes not only from a 'local' library, but from a nationwide selection
- freedom from advertising, e.g. where this freedom is allowed for in the charge for viewing the programme
- parental control of children's viewing to avoid porn or excessive violence
- better quality programmes because the financial return to the producer is directly related to the audience he attracts

Why are the viewers still waiting for better TV?

Proposal for a National Museum for the History of Innovation in Telecommunications and Information Technology*

The closure (in 1997) of the modest BT telecommunications history 'Showcase' museum in London was regretted by many of my BT colleagues as well as myself, and prompted me to write a letter to *The Times* (13.3.98) proposing a national museum as a replacement.

Writing my book *The Communications Miracle* had made me very much aware of the importance of this theme, and the support my *Times* letter received gave me an impulse to articulate the case for a national museum. This I saw as embracing the technology and system innovation that had led to today's worldwide communication and broadcasting systems, information technology and the Internet. It would include the major innovative contributions, whether from individual inventors, research organisations, universities, or commercial operating and manufacturing organisations. Whilst putting a major emphasis on the splendid UK contributions, it would put these into context against the world scene, notably from the USA.

My more detailed draft proposals are currently (1998) being considered, and receiving considerable support, by professional bodies such as the Royal Academy of Engineering and the Institution of Electrical Engineers, and universities, notably Imperial College and University College. HRH Prince Charles has approved in principle, no doubt influenced by his distinguished ancestor, Prince Albert, who founded the Natural History and Science Museums! The Ministry of Culture, Media and Sport, with the Commission for Galleries and Museums has made a preliminary study.

The Times 'Interface' writer Anjana Ahuja (22 July 1998) has expressed enthusiasm for the proposal in the following words:

---

* A short title might be 'National Museum for Electronic Communication'

'...it is such a splendid idea that one wonders why it has not been thought of before.'
'What better way of celebrating the end of the century than by celebrating one of its greatest achievements?'

The case for a new national museum with a distinctive title, location and identity, can be stated as follows:

(a) this technology, which has created today's worldwide communication, broadcasting and information access systems, is having and will continue to have, a profound impact on the way people live and work, and on national economies;

(b) there is urgent need, recognised by the Minister for Education and Employment, to train young people in the use of the information technology which will be an important part of their lives, and to produce an awareness of how this technology has been created. This, and especially the major contribution made by the UK, should be a part of general education – to which an imaginatively planned national museum could make a valuable contribution, pointing to the future as well as the past;

(c) the museum could be a valuable showcase for British Industry – important to the Ministry of Trade and Industry – involved in telecommunications, computers and information services, demonstrating not only substantial past achievements but also a forward-looking view – 'out of our past we build our future';

(d) and the museum could pay a long-neglected tribute – in a publicly visible form – to the many British pioneers who have helped to create one of mankind's greatest artefacts – the world communication system.

The museum could also have a regularly updated site via the Internet on the World-Wide Web, giving it international publicity and attracting visitors from other countries as well as the UK.

The location of the museum should offer convenient access for the majority of the population of the UK, and extensive parking space to encourage visitors, especially school coach parties. Possibilities might be the buildings of the former Naval College at Greenwich or the Millennium Dome itself.

The financing of such a museum would be a vital consideration; it is to be noted that organisations such as BT and Cable and Wireless, the computer industry, including IBM and Microsoft, commercial television broadcasting and the cable companies have made substantial fortunes by exploiting the innovations of the pioneers – it is high time that this debt was publicly acknowledged and repaid.

To sum up – a national museum for the History of Innovation in Telecommunications and Information Technology would give the nation pride in its remarkably creative past, provide a clear pointer for the future and have a valuable educative role, inspiring young people to make further creative contributions in a field of growing importance. It could provide a continuing and well-managed showcase for British expertise and commercial competence in many of the most important industries of our time. And not least, the museum could pay a lasting and deserved tribute to the pioneers whose work has made today's communication world possible.

6

Retirement and Community Life

How to Retire Gracefully

My retirement on 1 July 1975 at 64 years of age, after 40 years of active professional life, marked a change in my mode of living as profound and demanding as the step from college to work. From a life that had to be accommodated within a required time-framework, vistas of time unlimited suddenly appeared. From a life largely controlled by predetermined objectives came a prospect of setting one's own objectives and even cancelling them if necessary. However, it soon became clear that there were certain principles to be observed if this change was to be made successfully.

Firstly, one could not suddenly switch off a mind accustomed to thinking and writing about technical problems and the future of technology. In my case it was happily possible to continue for a time my visiting professorships at University College and Imperial College. And time became available to write two books and write about 'ideas not yet realised' and discuss them with colleagues.

Secondly, it was important to maintain a balance between mental and physical activities as a contribution to good health. With a sizable garden to look after, kitchen crops to grow, and a wooden boat to maintain and sail, this wasn't too difficult! And, when the weather was kind, there was the North Sea at Shingle Street to swim in.

Thirdly, there was a need to establish contacts leading to new friendships with the community around one, for which there was little time when professional activities were controlling. This turned out to be one of the most rewarding aspects of retirement and may be worthy of discussing in some detail.

Community Life

Our move to Bredfield, near Woodbridge, in rural Suffolk, in 1974 has been described in Chapter 3. This village, because of the remarkable degree of community spirit shown by its inhabitants, turned out to be an ideal location for former town dwellers such as Margaret and myself to learn about rural life and make new friends.

My introduction to this new world came about almost accidentally – out of sheer curiosity Margaret and I had attended, soon after we arrived in Bredfield, a meeting of the villagers in the Village Hall to discuss the formation of a 'Local Community Council'. (I have to admit I did not then know the differences between a 'Community Council', a 'Parish Council', a 'District Council' or a 'County Council'!)

The meeting was chaired by a Bertie Reid, an elderly gentleman who, with his wife Betty, had spent many years working for the Community Council of Suffolk establishing 100 or more Local Community Councils – work for which they were each awarded an MBE. The Local Community Councils were essentially voluntary organisations created to determine the needs of the communities living in and near villages, and to form projects and raise funds to meet these needs – e.g. to repair, improve or build a village hall. Bertie – with the skill to delegate that I later came to recognise as his hallmark – promptly enlisted me as his deputy. And so I became involved in rural community work, work that gave me much pleasure and satisfaction for the next 20 years.

Bertie had been a Physical Instructor in the Royal Navy and our paths had crossed, albeit unknowingly, when I was living in Portsmouth. He was a gentle man, who had a remarkable self-taught talent for painting both landscapes and miniatures. He and Betty taught me a great deal about the rural scene, and

141

he became my best friend. Sadly, Bertie died of Alzheimer's disease in 1996.

We Build a New Village Hall

When Margaret and I arrived in 1974 Bredfield already had a Village Hall and Playing Field, created on a gift of land by a local farmer, William Kenneth Richardson, and landowner Sir Denis Pilditch. They became Trustees of a Trust, set up in 1949, which defined the conditions of use of the Hall and Playing Field and which was managed by a Committee representing village organisations.

The Hall originally consisted of a wooden hut left over from the 1914–18 war and re-erected at a cost of about £100. Over the years until the 1970s it did excellent service for the village community; in particular it provided a home for the Bredfield Amateur Dramatic Society – 'BADS' – which worked miracles in producing plays and Christmas pantomimes on its minuscule stage.

But by 1977 it became obvious that a new village hall was needed; maintenance of the old hall was becoming difficult, and more space was needed by the thriving village organisations and a larger stage for BADS. Stimulated by Bertie Reid, the Village Hall Management Committee and the Bredfield and District Community Council, BDCC, agreed to build a new Village Hall, with BDCC taking a lead in fundraising by organising bring-and-buy sales, dances, concerts and similar activities. As Treasurer of the New Village Hall Building Trust Fund, I became heavily involved in the financial side of the project, which included inviting interest-free loans and covenants from villagers, getting a grant from Suffolk Coastal District Council and talking nicely to the National Westminster Bank Manager. And after managing a PO ED Research budget of some £15 million (little of which I actually saw), it was most refreshing to see envelopes containing gifts of £1 to £100 or more for the building fund coming through my home letterbox!

We were most fortunate in the voluntary work given by people living in and near Bredfield that went into the construction of the new Village Hall. A professional architect prepared plans and secured planning approval; local farmers produced tractors and diggers and prepared foundations; a bricklayer laid bricks; an electrician saw to the electrics and many villagers did painting work.

All went well and Bredfield New Village Hall was proudly opened on 2 July 1983, which included a Church service of dedication and a week of special events by village organisations.

The overall cost of the Hall was £46,000; it was valued for insurance purposes at £125,000. Of the cost £7,250 was contributed by grants from Suffolk Coastal District Council and the balance of £38,750 came from the villagers themselves – a fine tribute to the community spirit that existed in this small Suffolk village of some 200 families.

From my point of view, as a retirement activity this could not have been better. It involved much detailed keeping of financial accounts and preparing progress reports, writing letters inviting interest-free loans and soliciting local authority grants – and keeping an eye on what was actually being spent on bricks and mortar! But above all it meant making new friends amongst delightful, community-minded people and the satisfaction of helping to create a worthwhile community asset.

Suffolk Community Council and Suffolk ACRE

Soon after my arrival in Bredfield my good friend Bertie Reid propelled me into membership of the Village Halls Committee of Suffolk Community Council (SCC). The County Community Councils, which were largely voluntary organisations, with some financial and logistical support from government and local government sources, developed from the Rural Community Councils that were created after the 1914–18 war to help the young, the poor and the elderly in rural areas when Social Services such as we know today did not exist.

Membership of the Village Halls Committee of the SCC proved both educative and helpful. The members visited village halls in Suffolk to discuss at first hand problems of design, maintenance and finance, and to advise where professional help in these could be found. Advice on possible sources of grant aid for village hall projects was of course always welcome. The 'feedback' of such information to the Bredfield Village Hall Management Committee when it embarked on a new Hall, and later an extension, was particularly useful.

By the 1990s the Suffolk Community Council had become 'Suffolk ACRE' – Action With Communities in Rural England, still a largely voluntary charitable organisation, but with a small professional and highly dedicated staff. The mission of Suffolk ACRE has been stated as:

'Our mission is to support the growth of rural communities, encourage communal self-help and forge effective partnerships between agencies to enhance the quality of life.'

I was for several years a member of the Suffolk ACRE Management Committee, which gave me a better understanding and appreciation of the excellent work ACRE is doing in a wide range of areas – ranging from caring for the disabled and elderly, to the preservation of the rural environment, creation of rural employment and housing, and support of local, parish and town councils. In particular ACRE supports Government legislation that enhances the quality of life in rural areas.

Increasing importance in the rural scene is the use of computer-based information technology – 'telematics' and the 'tele-cottage'. This is creating new kinds of rural industry and providing a valuable stimulus to the local economy, as well as ready access to updated information – from jobs and social services to bus and train timetables – much needed by people living in the countryside. It has been a pleasure to be able to use one's professional background to support this theme, and an honour to be a member of Suffolk ACRE.

We Build an Extension to the Village Hall and a Voluntarily-run Village Shop

Notwithstanding the availability of supermarkets, villages with a population that includes many mothers with young children, and the elderly, often without means of transport, badly need a readily accessible village shop. When a commercial shop fails – as happened in Bredfield – this loss becomes acute and the Local Community Council BDCC looks for a solution.

A model was found at Polstead, Suffolk, where the villagers created a shop, housed at first in a trailer, and staffed by a rota of volunteers. At Bredfield BDCC first created a voluntarily-run shop in a Portacabin adjacent to the Village Hall. The success of this project over a period of some six years demonstrated in principle that a viable solution to the village shop problem had been found. But the Portacabin was too vulnerable to break-in and theft, and a more permanent solution was needed.

This was solved by a joint project between the Village Hall Management Committee (VHMC) and the BDCC to provide a purpose-built extension of the Village Hall to house the shop, and a Committee Room and Store Room for the Village Hall.

A Building Extension Trust Fund was established, of which I became Secretary/Treasurer with Chairmen of the BDCC, VHMC and Parish Council as Trustees. This worked very well and I was able to raise, with the help of Suffolk ACRE, some £18,000 of grant aid from Suffolk County and District Councils, the Rural Development Commission, the Sport and Arts Foundation and the Parish Council. The purpose-built extension was planned by a villager-architect, who dealt with planning permission and building regulations, and was built by a local builder at a cost of £30,000. The villagers contributed the balance of £12,000, mainly through BDCC fundraising.

The Village Shop was opened in its new location on 7 January 1995 and has continued to give excellent service to the villagers.

145

The Enchanted Village

In far-off Neolithic times
between primeval forest and sandy heath land
skin-clad men and women built rough shelters,
raised families and harvested crops,
and caught fish in a nearby river.

Roman warriors came and left behind
coins with an Emperor's profile.

Marauding Vikings sailed up the river
to pillage and plunder,
but found the place good
and some stayed.

Nearby a Saxon King was buried
with golden treasures of
unimaginable beauty.

In Medieval times farms grew and prospered,
houses of brick and windmills of wood
were built, blacksmiths and bakers,
saddlemakers and shoesmiths
plied their trades.

Kings and Queens reigned and the Village
celebrated the overthrow
of the Napoleonic tyrant.

Poets came and wrote immortal verse,
a Persian King planted roses
in the Village churchyard.

The Village lived through two World Wars
and gave sons for the common good.

The Church blessed marriages and births
and mourned the passing
of its sons and daughters.
The School nurtured the young
and gently eased their growth
to the adult world.

Craftsmen wrought in iron
elegant gates and balconies
that graced embassies
in distant lands.

And with the passing years
new technologies came,
broadcasting, television and satellites
linked the Village
to the outside World.

The Villagers built themselves a Hall
in which to sing and dance,
plan the future and keep alive
the spirit of community
in the Enchanted Village.

                                    Byron Haj

Visits to Abu Dhabi, United Arab Emirates 1980–84

One of the great advantages of retirement is the freedom it
gives to travel. In this Margaret and I were particularly fortunate, in that for a number of years we were able to visit our
daughter, son-in-law Brian, and grandchildren Laura and Paul
in Abu Dhabi during December and January, escaping the
worst of the English winter.

Brian, a shipping manager with British Petroleum, had
accepted a contract to work with the Abu Dhabi Gas Liquefaction Company, a consortium of Arab, British, French and
Japanese interests. The Company was created to collect and

exploit commercially the gas otherwise burnt off and wasted at oil wells, both on- and offshore, in the Arabian (formerly Persian) Gulf. It was a project of major technological problems, involving liquefaction of the gas at a large plant on Das Island in the Gulf and transporting the liquefied gas as far afield as Japan, where there was a ready market for its use, e.g. in cars and lorries.

The United Arab Emirates were originally created by the British in the early 1900s, who brought together several warring Arab states under the leadership of Sheik Zayed. With the vast income from oil, and well-advised government, the Emirates are one of the most prosperous and peaceful regions of the world, with excellent roads, schools and hospitals and a per-capita income for the Arabs that the inhabitants of most Western countries would envy.

For our grandchildren, up to the age of 12 there were excellent schools with English teachers; for the adults there were 'expatriate' clubs providing social activities and an opportunity to meet Arabs on a social footing. Christmas was especially enjoyable, with school plays and concerts, and parties galore.

The good roads across the desert regions and comfortable hotels enabled us to explore most of the Emirates, from the Gulf coast to the Straits of Hormuz in the North and the Indian Ocean in the East. One such journey took us some hundred miles across the 'empty quarter' to the desert town of Al Ain, which has a marvellous University built of marble and matching the Taj Mahal for architectural quality. And on to nearby Buraimi in the Sultanate of Oman, with its desert oasis and lush date, lemon and olive groves.

But the high spot was undoubtedly sailing in my son-in-law's Arab dhow to off-shore islands for sunbathing, swimming and barbecue picnics with other expatriates.

Above all, it was an opportunity to see at first hand something of the Arab and Islamic cultures – and a region of the world in which there was no unemployment and remarkably little crime.

7

The Women in My Life!

No autobiography can be regarded as complete, or even reasonably truthful, if it did not contain some account of the women in the author's life and their influence on his character, achievements and failings, but not, of course, should they be blamed for the latter!

In the beginning one must look to the maternal line – I think with admiration of my maternal grandmother, Caroline Clothier, in Somerset, widowed at 35 with five daughters and a crippled son to bring up in an age when Social Services and Income Support were nonexistent and the only family income was that derived from their own efforts.

My own mother, née Emily Clothier, I remember with love, affection and gratitude. It was she who taught me to read, realised the importance of a good education for her sons, instilled the Protestant 'work ethic' in both of us and encouraged us in our careers. In retrospect, I wish I had shown my appreciation and thanks more clearly when she was alive.

My wife Margaret has been a life-long, loyal companion who has shown quite remarkable tolerance to an often difficult and demanding husband! We have travelled the world, sailed through stormy seas, experienced the joys of family life and suffered the grief of a lost daughter together. Fortunately, in our later years, we had good health and were able to act as mutual 'carers'. So to Margaret, as well as my love, I owe much gratitude.

Sadly, Margaret died suddenly but peacefully on a normal happy day (19 August 1998); I held her hand in hospital and

149

thanked her for our life together as her life came quietly to a close. (See end of this chapter.)

Frances, my daughter, has been a great joy to both Margaret and myself – even though she has, at times, been my severest critic! She has had the good sense to provide us with an admirable son-in-law Brian, and two excellent grandchildren, Laura and Paul. As a family we get on very well together, free from the squabbles that bedevil so many of today's families.

In my career I have had very capable, but sometimes markedly different, lady secretaries. As Director I first had an elderly widowed lady who was dedicated to her work, which she carried out with great accuracy, often staying late to finish typing work. But she sometimes discouraged staff from seeking access to the Director at times when I would have preferred to hear at first hand about their problems. She was followed by a young lady who carried out her secretarial duties efficiently and handled staff with tact. But more than that, she sometimes saved her Director from getting into difficulties by using good commonsense – for example, I might, when faced with an unreasonable request from another Department, dictate an irate reply. This she would keep overnight, produce the draft the next morning with a very politely phrased suggestion that perhaps I might like to re-word it!

But, you say, there must have been other women in his life?

Of course there were – being a normal heterosexual male but with a romantic nature, I found most women fascinating and was liable to fall gently in love with any in my age group at the least provocation, not excluding the wives of colleagues. But let me quickly add, to calm any fears that my dear wife, family and friends may have had, these 'affairs' were wholly platonic and friendly. They brought fun, interest and a sparkle to life – and sometimes helped to ease over the rare 'rough patches' that occur even in the best of marriages.

Half a century later I can now look back at these gentle affairs calmly, with pleasure and much gratitude to the ladies involved – I can only hope they too found them enjoyable! As well as fun they sometimes included a little poetry – which may have had its inspiration with John Betjeman in similar circumstances. And as Laurie Lee recalled in *Cider With Rosie*, there is a certain sweetness in early romances that can never be replaced.

I remember especially kind-hearted 'Liz', the wife of a Post Office colleague, who married him soon after Madge and I were married. It was the kind of friendship that enabled us to talk freely about the problems that young marrieds encounter, and even to survive outrageous practical jokes. One of these involved breaking into their home whilst they were on honeymoon, finding an old suit of my colleague's and stuffing it with straw. This was then rigged up behind the front door of their home, and equipped with a violin that played the most excruciating noise to welcome them home!

In the summer of 1939 we went on a camping holiday with Liz and her husband in Dorset, in wet and windy weather. We had arranged to attend a friend's wedding in Bristol, but had great difficulty in starting the car at our muddy campsite. As a result we arrived late at the wedding, wet and dishevelled. I can still hear the bride saying 'Friends of the groom, I suppose', and the groom saying 'Friends of the bride, I suppose'!

My friendship with Liz even survived when, one Easter, she turned up at our home wearing the most outrageous heart-shaped hat as an Easter 'bonnet' and when she asked 'Did I like it?' I replied, 'My dear, you look just like the Queen of Tarts!'

Years later, when we had moved to East Anglia, I became friendly with Pauline, an unmarried lady living in a cottage near our home. Pauline had great artistic talent, her line drawings of local listed buildings were in considerable demand, and some appeared in a book about the homes of notable people in East Anglia called *They Lived Here*. I have two of her line drawings, one of Lavenham Guildhall and the other of the Steel Yard Weigh Point in Woodbridge. She also painted with considerable skill, and a watercolour of poppies that has an unusual three-dimensional depth appears on my hall wall.

Pauline was Headmistress of a local primary school, and I was once invited to appear as Father Christmas to present

151

gifts, which I did following my usual routine of asking the class if little Harry, about to receive his present, 'Had been a good boy?', the normal response being a resounding 'Yes'. However, at the bottom of the sack of presents was one for Pauline, and I could not resist asking the class, 'Has she been a good girl?' The more than resounding 'No' must have been heard a mile or more outside the school!

A lady who helped me to get to know the rural scene and became an important part of my life in Bredfield was Betty, the wife of Bertie Reid, my best friend for more than 20 years and who, as recounted earlier, was responsible for my becoming involved in Local Community Council work and Suffolk Community Council.

Betty is a real countrywoman; she loves the beauty of the Suffolk countryside, adores her dogs and maintains with skill and energy her large garden. She enjoys books and poetry, especially those dealing with the countryside – but complains she hasn't time to read them all! She has a considerable history of being involved herself with the Rural Community Councils and their work for the poor and disadvantaged in rural communities.

She taught me, a townee for most of my days, much about village life and rural matters but, being an intelligent lady, is curious about the modern world. It has been my pleasure to try to answer her queries, for example about the incredible universe we live in, and even how does e-mail work!

There was a vivid example of the value of e-mail when she was suddenly taken ill; by e-mail I was able quickly to contact her daughter in America and help to arrange a visit.

Sadly she lost, in tragic circumstances, her husband Bertie, who in his late 80s developed Alzheimer's disease, and I lost my best friend. In Bertie's memory I am seeking to support research on Alzheimer's, which seems to me to be one of the greatest of the scourges of mankind (and from which my own mother eventually suffered).

But to go back to happier events. An early meeting with Betty was as she emerged from a coffee shop in Woodbridge, laden with parcels and 'asking for a porter', which I was happy to supply! There were many later, pleasant, meetings in the coffee shop. Perhaps the poems that follow, if not brilliant as poetry, may convey something of the quality of a good friendship.

The Coffee Shop

Where friends and chance acquaintances
meet and greet.
Exchange news and share troubles,
so making a quiet eddy
in life's fast moving stream.
And hear in imagination,
the hiss of steam
from the railway station buffet urn,
the rattle of the tea cups,
and the sounds of passing trains.
Where Celia Johnson as the housewife
and Trevor Howard as the doctor,*
not forgetting lifetime partners,
found mutual affection,
fun and friendship.

Byron Haj

A Village Friendship

She, whose early days were spent in London,
came to Anglia and learned to care
for the creatures of the countryside
and the rural scene.

He, born in a dockyard town,
grew as an apprentice
amid the grey, gaunt shapes of battleships.
She found a lifetime vocation in community work,

---

* In the film of *Brief Encounter* by Noel Coward

to which she brought a clear mind,
a profound sense of justice,
and a keen regard for the rule of law.

He, from small beginnings
as a boy making crystal radio sets,
found a rewarding career
that led to satellites orbiting the globe,
bringing voices and living images
from far corners of the Earth.

They met by chance in a Suffolk village
and found common interests
in books, music and poetry.

She helped him understand,
enjoy and contribute
to rural community life,
adding a new dimension
to his later years.

He opened her eyes to the
awe-inspiring beauty of the Universe
and the great unanswered questions
of 'how' and 'why' created.

There was fun and joy in their friendship,
sometimes illuminated by
'today's funny story'.

And occasional 'tiffs' when
strong wills clashed,
resolved made friendship stronger.

Both had loyal lifetime partners
for whom to care and share
life's joys and sadnesses.

154

There was perhaps
a hint of passion in their
occasional embrace, remembering
the 17th century poet:*

'Behind my back I hear
Time's winged chariot,
hurrying near.
The grave is a private and a silent place
but none, I fear, do there embrace!'

Byron Haj

A Last Farewell

Margaret Bray, b. 14 Aug. 1911 d. 19 Aug. 1998 (See plate 16)

My dear wife Margaret collapsed suddenly from an aneurism
of the aorta on a normal happy day at home, a few days after
her 87th birthday, and passed away peacefully an hour later in
Ipswich Hospital. I held her hand as her breathing became
slower and thanked her for all the happiness she had brought
me in the 62 years of our wonderful life together.

Inevitably it was for me a time of great sadness and loss,
but I had the support of our daughter Frances, the family
and many good friends. The funeral service in St Andrew's
Church, Bredfield, was conducted with great sensitivity before
a full congregation by the Rural Dean, the Rev. Robert
Clifton. The service included the poem 'A Last Farewell to
Margaret'.

---

* Andrew Marvell

A Last Farewell to Margaret
1911–1998

After more than 60 years of happy marriage
The time has come to say
Farewell to a most devoted wife.
And to express a heart-felt gratitude
For her love, her tolerance,
Her constant companionship
Our lovely daughters and
The joy she brought into our lives.

Together we shared heart-breaking grief
When our younger daughter,
An intelligent and happy child
Died at eleven years of age.

Together we travelled the World
When my profession took me to
International conferences,
And a Commonwealth Fellowship
Enabled us to travel free-lance
For three months in the USA.

Together we sailed my yacht
Through stormy seas to safe harbours.

Family holidays were always a great joy
First when our children were young
And later when we were joined by grandchildren.

Margaret loved painting and had real talent.
The walls of our house are adorned
With her pictures and will remind me
Of happy past times.

She enjoyed talking to people, young and old,
And her work in the Bredfield community,
With the WI and Over 60s,
Gave her much pleasure.

Perhaps we shall meet again
In some un-imaginable new world
Beyond our present ken.
Till then her memory will remain
The fondest memory in my heart.

John

8

Politics

My political sympathies have varied with the years – perhaps not surprisingly in view of my namesake, the famous Vicar of Bray, recalled in the verse:

'And this is law I will maintain
Until my dying day, sir,
That whatsoever King shall reign,
I will be Vicar of Bray, sir.

In my case the changes have been occasioned, not by changing monarchs or governments, but by a slow process of political education and learning.

Early Views

Being members of a working-class family, my parents' views were more to the 'left' than 'right', tempered by a strong feeling of loyalty to the Crown engendered by the family Naval tradition.

I began to take an interest in politics as an apprentice in Portsmouth Dockyard and was much influenced by Alderman Lacey JP, the father of a teenage friend, Sidney, who lived near my home in Milton, on the east side of Portsea Island. Alderman Lacey was a much respected Justice of the Peace who also worked as a craftsman in Portsmouth Dockyard. Sidney and I often helped his canvassing for municipal elections by delivering leaflets and, I regret to say, heckling at political meetings!

Alderman Lacey and I often cycled to work together, and during these long rides he would enlighten me on the principles of Socialism. Ringing phrases such as 'from each according to his ability and to each according to his need' seemed to me then a true expression of social justice. It was not until much later that I began to realise that to give 'to each according to his need', wealth had first to be created and Socialism, with its closely regulated, planned from the centre, structure, was not a very efficient way of creating the necessary wealth.

It was the Bishop of Portsmouth, no less, who began to make me wonder whether Socialism might not be an effective remedy for the social injustices of the day. At a Dockyard School prize-giving in my fourth year, the Bishop proclaimed that 'any man who was not a Socialist until he was 21 years of age ought to have his heart examined, but if he was a Socialist after the age of 21 he ought to have his head examined!' This set me thinking and reading more widely about politics; one of my sources, bought regularly out of an apprentice's meagre wage, was the now defunct BBC journal *The Listener* which gave in print the content of broadcast radio talks by politicians and commentators with a wide range of political views.

Changing Political Views: The Postwar Years

Victory in the Second World War had left the United Kingdom economy in a dire state, the people war-weary and feeling that after the deprivations and sacrifices of the war years they deserved a better deal. The rejection in the Parliamentary Election of 1945 of the Conservatives under Sir Winston Churchill – the man who had done more to win the war for the Allies than any other person – resulted in the Labour Government of 1945–50.

Disappointment with Socialism in practice, and the excessive power of the trade unions that led to a succession of strikes in the postwar period and virtually brought the country to its economic knees, made me consider political alternatives. For a

159

time Liberalism appealed to me for its emphasis on personal freedom and humanism, but the poor performance of the Liberal Party in the 1945 Parliamentary Election indicated that it was unlikely to achieve effective political power.

To its credit, the Labour Government of 1945–50 initiated the Beveridge Report, prepared by Sir William Beveridge, that made recommendations for social reforms of far-reaching importance, including a National Health Service, social insurance, family allowances and full employment. The implementation of the National Health Service by the Labour Minister of Health, Aneurin Bevan, in 1946 gave the United Kingdom a health service that, despite financial problems, is the envy of the world.

Realising the need to remove excessive trade union power and the straightjacket of over-regulation if the economy was to afford the social reforms introduced by the Labour Party, my political views moved to support of the Conservative Party and Margaret Thatcher's Government of 1975. Her measures to reduce the power of the trade unions – notably following the miners' strike of 1984 – and introduce the privatisation of many sectors of the nationalised industries, resulted in a thriving economy and consistently falling unemployment, unmatched in the rest of Europe.

Lady Thatcher has a reputation for toughness in achieving her aims, perhaps best illustrated by her own words. In paying a well-deserved tribute to Sir William ('Willie') Whitelaw, her friend and advisor, she was heard to remark to her male Cabinet that 'Of course, every Prime Minister needs a Willie'!

Politics and the Post Office

During my time with the Post Office (1935–75) it was a Civil Service Department, under the control of a Postmaster General who was directly responsible to Parliament. Its services included Posts, Telephones and Telegraphs, and the regulation of sound and television broadcasting. It was financed by

Parliamentary vote and subject to strict Treasury control of investment and expenditure.

Most of the equipment needed for the various services was purchased from private industry, on the basis of detailed technical specifications prepared by the PO and lowest price contracts. However, Treasury control of ongoing expenditure made it difficult to invest in advance for equipment, e.g cables, radio-relays or exchanges, to meet foreseen but not proven demand. This was especially onerous when new telecommunication systems of advanced design, e.g. exchange System X, were involved[4].

The technology advances of the 1970s – optical fibre cables, communication satellites, digital techniques and the microchip – led to a vast expansion of the scale and character of telecommunication that made the state-controlled PTT structure inappropriate and inefficient. The 'wind of change' brought about by the massive growth of worldwide telecommunications, information technology and the Internet made it essential for economic survival to find a new political structure.

The first political move, in 1981, was to convert the PTT into separate 'Postal' and 'Telecommunication' organisations, with Telecommunication having the status of a Public Corporation. I had a minor role in this, in that it fell to me to convince the last Postmaster General, the Rt Hon John Stonehouse MP, that the new Corporation must have a strong research capability!

The 'privatisation' policy of the Thatcher Government provided the next step with the creation of British Telecom in 1984, on a scale and with the capability to function as a world leader in its field and to cope with competition, both nationally and internationally. I feel a little proud to have left a research capability at the BT Martlesham Laboratories that is one of the key foundations on which British Telecom future is based.

I only hope that Oftel, the Government telecommunication regulator, will some day give BT the freedom to compete fairly with its rivals in such matters as the unrestricted transmission of video (television) over the BT network, including the 'view-on-demand' television service, and the use of the environmentally-friendly millimetric microwaves for local area distribution of telephone and video service.

Meanwhile, perhaps I must be content to note that, come what may, my home connection to the World-Wide Web is through a humble footway box marked on its cast-iron cover:

General Post Office Telephones!

9

Religion and Cosmology

Religion plays a part in most people's lives, if only at times of marriage, birth of children, death and family crises; my parents' approach to religion was of this low-key kind. The family tradition favoured Baptist teaching, and my brother and I were sent to Sunday School in our young days, from which I regret to say I occasionally 'played hookey' when the sun was shining and outdoors was more attractive!

At my secondary school assemblies for hymns, prayers and a brief address by the Headmaster, following the Church of England format, conveyed at least an outline of Christianity. But for the most part my religious views as a young man were unformed and only became more positive much later in life as a result of experience, discussion and reading.

God and Christianity

Much as I am aware of the majesty and scale of the created universe and felt the need for an understanding of how it came into existence and the purpose of human life, I have not felt the need for a personal 'God' to praise for the good things of life, to seek help in a crisis or blame for the evil that manifestly exists in the world. Nor have I a desire for eternal life after death, much as I would like to say thank you again to my parents and express my love to a deceased wife and daughter.

Primitive man clearly felt the need for a 'God' to protect him from the dangers of his life and blame for the crops that failed, even resorting to human sacrifice to propitiate an angry deity.

With the gradual growth of human intelligence over many millennia, the need grew for an explanation of the origin and purpose of human life, and guidance for its better conduct.

From this need emerged the great religions of the world – Christianity, Islam, Judaism, Hinduism and Buddhism – each of these proclaimed a God introduced by a prophet and a written code. In the case of Christianity the prophet was Jesus Christ and the Bible, for Islam it was Muhammad and the Koran.[5]

Christianity and the Bible

Christianity has provided a code of moral principles – recorded in the Bible and exemplified by the Ten Commandments and the Sermon on the Mount – that has been, and will continue to be, the bedrock of Western civilisation. The architect of its creation two millennia ago – Jesus Christ – was probably the greatest human genius yet to exist, transcending such creative intellectual giants as Beethoven, Einstein and Shakespeare.

Whether Jesus Christ or his birth were 'divine' or not, there is no doubt that he was a very real and living person, a man of great charm, compassion and ability to communicate. However, the idea that the Gospels of the Bible were eye-witness accounts of Jesus's life is no longer believed by serious theologians and biblical scholars. This is demonstrated by the many inconsistencies that exist between different accounts of the same event, and errors of translation, geography and dating that close examination has revealed.[6]

None of this constitutes a denial of Jesus's existence or the importance of his message, but it is a warning not to take the texts too literally. This applies to the stories of the 'miracles' – beautiful as they are – they were the means by which he got his message over to a pastoral people of limited knowledge and education. And the Biblical story of his own resurrection from the dead (possibly in reality a coma) may well have been a vivid means of impressing himself and his message on the minds of his disciples. It is what he did during his life on Earth and the moral principles that he taught that matter – not how he arrived here or the myths that arose afterwards.

The Values of Religion

Religious faith and practice have clearly been of immense value in civilising the human race by providing a code of morals that emphasise the virtues of honesty, compassion and justice, support the family and condemn evil-doing. In these respects the Bible and the Koran have much in common.

The practice of prayer gives solace and comfort to the bereaved and unfortunate when no other help may be available. The act of worship, expressing faith in God, has inspired many to lives of dedication and self-sacrifice to the benefit of the human race. Faith has inspired the building of great cathedrals and modest churches, and the composing of hymns expressing human longing for more perfect lives.

But there are undesirable aspects to the practice of religion that have to be recognised and will need to be avoided if civilisation is to survive.

Problems Created by Religion

The many existing different interpretations of the wording of the Bible Gospels – and other texts such as the Koran – have given rise to a multiplicity of religious sects, each with its own identity and group of adherents, convinced that theirs alone is the true version approved by God. This has created much bitter strife, both within the framework of the world religions such as Christianity and Islam, and between the major religions themselves. History has shown that this conflict has had a devastating effect on the growth of civilisation, for example:

- the Crusades of the 12th century, during which the Christians and Muslims fought for possession of the cities of the Holy Land

165

- the Papal-inspired Inquisition of the Middle Ages, in which heretics against the Catholic faith were hunted, tortured and killed
- anti-Semitism, in which Jews throughout Europe were subject to pogroms during the Middle Ages and massacre in the holocaust of the Second World War
- the atrocities carried out in recent years, contrary to the guidance of the Koran, by extreme Islamic fundamentalists in Algiers, Egypt and Palestine
- the Protestant–Catholic divide in Northern Ireland

In an age in which nuclear bombs may have put mass destruction in the hands of so-called religionists and terrorists, it becomes of vital importance to find ways by which civilisation can continue to evolve without destroying itself.

In the millions of years of evolution of the human race it was the 'survival of the fittest' – that is, those best able to find food and defeat enemies – that was the guiding principle, as Darwin showed in his *Origin of the Species*. Fortunately, the growth of human intelligence and the ability to communicate now make possible a wiser and more humane principle for the development and improvement of the human race in the millennia to come.

History, and the manifest existence of much evil in the world, has demonstrated that faith in a benevolent God and the pursuit of diverse religions is not enough. The human race must use its evolving intelligence, rather than the driving force of 'survival of the fittest', to ensure progress towards a true civilisation.

A primary need is the creation of a universally accepted code of moral principles, based on concepts such as respect for truth, justice, compassion and care for others and the family.

These concepts are already included in Christianity, as exemplified by the teachings of Jesus Christ, the Islamic religion in the Koran, and in other world religions.

They need to be developed to create a basis for world moral law, to regulate the dealings between groups within nations and between nations themselves. Without it, and bearing in mind the ever present shadow of the nuclear bomb, the Planet Earth may some day be discovered by visitors from space as once the home of a civilisation that destroyed itself.

Cosmology and Religion

The picture of the universe that has emerged from astronomical and physical science studies, cosmology, during the last half century is one of incredible complexity and beauty – vindicating Sir James Jeans' saying that 'the Universe is more mysterious than we can possibly imagine'.

Cosmology has revealed a universe beginning with a 'big bang', an explosion in empty space some 15 billion years ago that created the basic atomic particles which in millions of years formed into a host of star galaxies, each containing billions of stars. Our Milky Way is but one of the galaxies, and the Sun only a minor star in the Milky Way. The Earth itself came into being some 4.5 billion years ago, with *Homo sapiens* evolving from primitive life forms a mere few million years ago.

The 'big bang' created a very weak background of radio noise, only 3 degrees above absolute zero temperature, that pervades all space. It was discovered by Bell Laboratories communication scientists in 1978 when testing a microwave dish aerial, thus providing proof of the reality of the 'big bang'. And the Hubble telescope now orbiting the Earth is giving ever more remarkable and detailed information about the structure of even the most distant star galaxies[7].

The story thus revealed differs so vividly from the account of creation given in Genesis that the Bible story, beautiful though it is, cannot now be regarded as having a foundation in reality. And it is difficult to reconcile creation itself as being attributable to a God, as described in the Bible.

The fact that the universe contains countless millions of stars which, like our Sun, may have planets capable of sustaining life, albeit very different from that on Earth, raises questions of great interest.

If the life forms on other planets of the star galaxies are intelligent, as they may well be, the probability is that they are far more advanced in civilisation than mankind. If the problems of communication and space travel are resolvable, they may yet save mankind from the self-destruction that it appears to be heading for.

10

A Final Summing-up

The last page of *The Communications Miracle* ends with the words:

'From a schoolboy building a crystal radio set to an engineer helping to span the Atlantic with live television for the first time ever, what a marvellous journey it has been.'

More than 20 years of retirement have provided opportunities to extend one's experience and knowledge by reading and writing, learning more about community life in a rural environment and pondering about the future of mankind in a universe of ever-growing complexity and beauty.

Now that I can look back on a lifetime of more than 85 years, what can one say but:

'What a fascinating, unpredictable and fulfilling experience it has been – wouldn't have missed it for the world!'

The time has come when I must thank all those who have helped to make my journey so rewarding, from my marvellous parents, my loyal, supportive and tolerant wife, my kindly daughter, son-in-law and grandchildren, and the many teachers, colleagues and friends who held out helping hands along the way.

And now, following the loss of my dear wife I live on my own, kindly help from John the gardener and Liz the domestic help lady are keeping my home running comfortably. Friends in the village keep up my morale with friendly chat – and of course there's always the village shop and its coffee bar wherein to meet them!

And I'm learning, having abandoned car driving for good, to use a versatile electric trolley to get about the village – much cheaper to run and better for the environment!

I must thank John Henderson and Dr Gerry White, former PO/BT colleagues, for many helpful discussions and help in overcoming the mysteries of Microsoft Windows 95 via which this book was composed. Jim Maslin, former PO draughtsman at Dollis Hill, deserves thanks for the charming sketches that appear on pages 52, 66 and 67. My thanks also go to Top Floor Studio, Woodbridge, for creating, from a holiday snapshot, the excellent portrait of my wife Margaret that appears as a colour plate.

As a believer in Lincoln's 'government of the people, by the people, for the people', the slow march of mankind towards civilisation continues to interest me. But at times one feels a sense of despair at the continuing tide of ever more destructive wars, the power of terrorists to destroy, the evils of mass genocide in Africa and Yugoslavia, the disastrous rule of tyrants in Iraq and some African states, and the never-ending antagonism between rival religions.

The expanding powers of communication and information access offered by the Internet and the World-Wide Web may well be important tools for improving the quality of human intelligence and making known, at an early stage, world trouble spots so that the powers determined to create a more civilised world can take appropriate remedial action.

But it is early days to expect mankind to achieve a truly civilised state – perhaps millennium 3000 may see some real progress. After all, it took thousands of years for the human race to learn to read, write and count. I would dearly love to return to Earth (spiritually, but not bodily) at intervals of, say, 100 years, to see what progress had been made, and if necessary, to promote action!

Meanwhile there are my 'good causes', such as a 'National Museum for Electronic Communication, and the need for a 'view-on-demand' approach to TV viewing to pursue, and perhaps another book to write (the story of the origins of the Internet still needs to be put on record)!

Although I greatly miss the company of my wife, and lesser things such as sailing my own boat and swimming in the North Sea, I intend – like Voltaire – to continue happily to 'cultivate my garden', watch the changing skies, listen to the song of birds and chat with friends.

References

(1) 'John Bray Makes 30-mile Navigational Error', by John Bray, *Yachting Monthly*, July 1978
(2) *Magic of the Swatchways* by Maurice Griffiths, first pub. George Allen and Unwin, 1932; pub. Adlard Coles Nautical, 1997
(3) *Secret Waters* by Arthur Ransome, pub. Red Fox, 1993
(4) *Monopoly and Competition in British Telecommunications* by John Harper, pub. Pinter, 1997
(5) The *Encarta 95* encyclopedia computer disk provides excellent surveys and detailed information concerning cosmology and religion, including an article on 'God' by John Macquarnie.
(6) Letter by R. Stafford, *Daily Mail*, 1 Jan., 1998
(7) *The Communications Miracle* by John Bray, pub. Plenum of New York and London, 1995, describes in Chapter 15, p. 244, the discovery of the background radio noise in space that supports the 'big bang' theory of the creation of the Universe.

INDEX

Abu Dhabi, Visit to 147
Admiralty Research Establishment 4
Admiralty Service 27
Advertising Competition, TV 134
Albert Memorial 24
American Telephone and Telegraph Co 50, 59, 60, 69
Andover, Maine 79
Anglia East, Move To 123
Appleton, Sir Edward 48
Apprentices, Dockyard, Ex 4YA 11, 25
Arnold 7966, poem 121
Armstrong 51
Autobiography ix
Ayers, E.W. 90

Baird, J.L. 63
Baldock, PO Radio 39
Baxter, Raymond 81
Beam Bending 44
Bell Telephone Labs 49, 60, 90
Bennett, Alan 95
Bideford, Devon 6
Bishop, H. Sir 22
Black, J.S. 60
Bletchley Park 46
Blue Streak Rocket 76
Booth, C.F. Capt. 38, 81
Bray, Elizabeth 7, 119, poem 121
Bray, Frances 80, 120
Bray, Margaret 116, 149, 155, poem 156, 169
Bray, William James 3, 6, 7
Bredfield 124

Brett, P.R. 97
British Commonwealth Conference (Satellite Communications) 77
British Telecom x, 94, 161
Broadcasting 7, 85
Brockbank, R.A. 89
Burt, E.G.C. 76
Byron Haj 113

Cadbury, K. 95
Catermole, K. Prof. 94
CCIR Study Group IX 55
City and Guilds of London Institute 101
Centre Nationale des Télécommunication CNET 56, 79
Clarke, A.C. 71, 109
Clothier, Emily 3
Code Breakers 45
College, City and Guilds 20
College, Imperial x
College, Royal Naval 12, 27
Colossus 46
Colour TV, TransAtlantic 82
Commonwealth Fund Fellowship, USA 58
Communications Miracle, The (book) 111
Community Life 140
Cooke, Alistair 58
Cooling Marshes 40
Coombes, A. Dr 89
Co-ordination of Valve Development Committee 53
Cosmology and Religion 167

173

Crystal Radio Set 8

Daughter, Loss of 120
Device Technology 84, 87
Digital Techniques x, 88
Direction Finding, Radio 43
Director of Research x, 90
Dockyard, Naval, Portsmouth 14
Dollis Hill Research Station 31, 33, 42
Dreiser, T. 28

Earp, Margaret 116
Eastwood, Eric Dr 10
Eckersley, P.P. Capt 7
Electrician, the Boy (book) 10
English Channel, first microwave link 56
Essex University, first Telecom Chair 94
European Launcher Developt. Org. 76

Fading Machine 39
Family Tree 7
Flowers, Tom Dr 46
Floyd, C.F. 91
Fortescue, L. Prof. 23
Frequency Modulation 51
Friis, H.T. Dr 40, 60

German Fleet 4
German, Sir Ronald 82
Gill, A.J. Sir 26
God and Christian Religion 163
Goonhilly Sat. Earth Station 79
Grandparents 6

Hobbies x
Husband, Tom Dr 80

Ideas Not Yet Realized 132
Imperial College x
Inland Radio Branch (POED) 67
Institution of Electrical Engineers 3, 99

International Standardization of Radio-Relay Systems 54
Irvine, J.M. 13

Jones, David Dr 10
John Bray Lecture Theatre 93

Kompfner, R. Dr 53
Kelly, Dr 60

Law, H.B. 90
Layzell, A. 111
Learning Life, A. 3
Lecture Theatre, the John Bray 93, 112
Lecture Tours S. Africa '72 95
Lecture Tours Australia '73 96
Lewis, N.W. Dr 65
Lines, A.W. Dr 76
Loudspeaker, homemade 17
Love, Marriage and Children 116

Marriage 117
Maritime Radio Conference 69
MacDonald, Ramsey PM 24
Mallet, E. Dr 23
Manchester-Kirk O'Shotts Radio-Relay 53
Martlesham PO/BT Laboratories 91, 161
May, C. Director BT 93
McKenzie, Mr 13
Meacon 45
Memoirs of a Telecommunication Engineer John Bray (book) 111
Men of Mathematics, E.T. Bell (book) 13
Merriman, J.H.H. Prof., BT Board 44, 51
Metson, G. Dr, Director of Research, PO 33
Microchip Technology x, 84
Microwave Radio Communication 50, 68
Milton, Portsmouth 5

174

Multiple Unit Steerable Antenna (MUSA) 40
Molnar, J. Dr, Bell Labs. 90
Moon as an Artificial Satellite 48
Mumford, A. Sir, E in C, POED 38, 47
Museum, National for Electronic Communication 137

National Aeronautics and Space Administration, USA NASA 76
Night on Walton Channel, poem 113

O'Brian, Patrick, Author 109
O'Neill, Gene Dr, Bell Labs 80, 111
Optical Fibre Cables x, 88
Orbital Radio Relays 71

Personal Life, A 105
Personal TV-Video Receiver 132
Pirates, TV 65
Pierce, J.S., Dr 60
Pleumer Bodou 79
PO Electrical Engineers Journal 87
Poems 113, 121, 146, 153, 156
Poetry, Reading and Writing 107
Politics 158
Portsmouth Naval Dockyard x, 11, 14
Postal Engineering Research 89
Post-Master General 63
Post Office Engineering Dept. POED x, 26
Post Office Research Branch 86
Post-War Years 119
Preface ix
Probationary Assistant Engineer POED 31
Professional Life 31
Pulse-Code Modulation 88

Queen Elizabeth HRH 82, 93

'Rabitting' 16
Radio, Crystal Set 8
Radio Echo Direction Finder (aircraft) 46
Radio Experimental Branch, Dollis Hill 34, 38
Radio Hobbies 16
Radio Services, PO 35
Radley, Gordon Sir 42
Radio Society, the Guilds 22
Reading, Writing and Poetry 107
Reid, Betty and Bertie 141, 152
Reigh, John Sir 7
Relay Satellite 77
Religion and Cosmology 167
Research Branch, POED 86
Retirement 97, 140
Rodgers, D.C. 53
Royal Academy of Engineering 102
Royal Aircraft Establishment 76
Royal Scholarship 12, 18
Rudge, Alan Dr, Deputy Chairman BT 112
Rugby Radio Station 35

Sailing Hobby x, 126
Satellite Communication Systems x, 54, 71
Sail Making 6
Sanders, John and Jane 7
Saxton, J.A. Dr 100
Scapa Flow 4
Schoolboy 5
Science Museum 21
School, Primary 5
School, Royal Dockyard, Portsmouth 11
School, Southern Secondary, Portsmouth 11
Services Electronic Research Labs. SERL 80
Sheriff, R.C. 28
Shute, Neville 109
Sjøhest 127
Southsea 5, 8

175

Space Communication Systems
    Branch, POED 74
Sputnik 74
Standard Telecom. Labs 50
Stanesby, Harold 55
Stonehouse, John PMG 94
Suffolk Community Council ACRE
    xi, 143
Sutcliffe, Pauline 151
Summing Up 169
Syncom Satellite 82

Taylor, F.J.D. 76, 77, 79
Technological Advances, Post-War
    84
Telecommunication Union,
    International 54
Television Advertising 134
Television, Baird Receiver 17
Television Licences, TV Pirates 65
Television, More Channels and
    Better TV? 135
Television, Post Office and 63
Telstar Satellite 77
Thomson, W.E. 79
Tillman, J.R. Dr 90
Timmis, A.C. Capt. 42

Turnbull, R.W. 97
Travelling-wave Tube 53, 80
Trethowan, Ian ITV 81

Universe ix, 167

Vallance, Sir Iain, Chairman BT
    112
Valves, Radio 16
Vernon Naval Est. 19
Viewdata (Prestel) 88
Village Hall xi, 142
Village, the Enchanted, poem 146
Village, Shop 145
Village, a Friendship, poem 153

Warr, Earl de la PMG 65
War Years 42, 118
Watson-Watt, Robert Sir 46
Webster, Albert 91
Wells, H.G. 4, 108
White, Robert 48
World-Wide Web Site 102
Women, the, In My Life! 149

Yeovil 4

176